Patterns of the Hypnotic Techniques of Milton H. Erickson, M.D.

Vol. II

**John Grinder, Judith DeLozier,
and Richard Bandler**

Grinder & Associates

Published by
Grinder & Associates
PO Box 67295
Scotts Valley, CA 95067

Master Distributor
Metamorphous Advanced Product Services
PO Box 10616
Portland, OR 97296-0616

Copyright © 1977 by Meta Publications
Editorial and Art Direction by Lori Stephens
Cover illustration by Robert B. Dilts
Printed in the United States of America

Bandler, Richard.
   Patterns of the hypnotic techniques of Milton H. Erickson, M.D. /
by Richard Bandler and John Grinder.
       p. cm.
   Originally published: Cupertino, Calif. : Meta Publications, 1975.
   Includes bibliographical references (p.   ).
   ISBN 1-55552-053-7
   1. Hypnotism—Therapeutic use. 2. Erickson, Milton H.
   I. Grinder, John. II. Title.
RC495.B32   1996
615.8'512—dc20   96-25682

*Acknowledgment is gratefully made to Milton H. Erickson and Herbert S. Lustig for
permission to reprint a photograph and the transcripts from The Artistry of Milton
H. Erickson, M.D., copyright 1975 by Milton H. Erickson, M.D., and Herbert S.
Lustig, M.D., Ltd.*

We dedicate this book

with the deepest

respect

to

Ghost Roger Drassett,

a purple rose,

the Palo Verde tree

and

a different perspective.

Table of Contents

PART I

Introduction

Each of us as a human being is constantly subjected to enormous amounts of information. A portion of this stimulation is the result of the contact we have with the parts of the world which we are able to sense with our sensory channels. The amount of information available from our ongoing experience greatly exceeds our ability to sense our experience *consciously* . In fact much of the process of learning and growing is our ability to sense regularity or pattern in our experience and to develop programs within ourselves to cope effectively with the world at the *unconscious* level of behavior. For example, your ability to read and understand this very sentence is a program which at one point in your life you were unable to perform. You went through the task of learning to recognize first the letters, then the words and finally the phrases and sentences of English. Associated with each of these steps were the specific eye scanning patterns which were appropriate. Learning to associate a certain visual input with a set of meanings which they represent was a relatively long and arduous task. Your skill in reading rapidly and meaningfully depends in large part on your ability to operate those lower level patterns of eye scanning and letter recognition *unconsciously*. The vast bulk of our everyday lives is occupied with the execution of tremendously complex patterns of unconscious behavior. The ability we have to enjoy our experience and engage in the activities which each of us find interesting and pleasing would in large part be lost if we did not have the ability to program ourselves to carry out certain complex patterns of behavior for execution at the unconscious level of behavior. Imagine how cluttered our experience would be, for example, if it were necessary for us to consciously maintain the rate and depth of our breathing, the tonus of our muscles, the level of our blood sugar . . .

The process of creating programs which are useful to us — the learning process — is an ongoing process of change. We refer to this process as *modeling.*Modeling occurs both at the conscious and unconscious levels of behavior. The process of learning to understand and speak our native language is an example of the process of unconscious modeling. The process of learning to read and to spell is, for most people, an example of conscious modeling, much of what is learned is the sequencing and organization of lower level patterns of behavior already available at the unconscious level of behavior. For example, children learning to spell are not explicitly taught to form mental images of the words they are learning — that is, to employ their visualization strategies — yet, children who succeed in becoming excellent spellers employ this skill unconsciously. A young athlete learning to run the 100 meter dash is learning how to sequence and utilize patterns of muscle movements already available at the unconscious level of behavior. His ability to run the 100 meter dash is learning how to sequence and utilize patterns of muscle movements already available at the unconscious level of behavior. His ability to run the 100 meter dash at maximum speed will depend in large part on his ability to make unconscious the patterns of sequencing of those patterns of unconscious behavior already available.

The outcome of modeling is the creation of a series of models which are largely unconscious which each of us use to organize our experience and cope effectively with the worlds of our experience. As we have demonstrated in other work (see *Structure of Magic*, volumes I and II, *Patterns of the Hypnotic Techniques of Milton H. Erickson, M.D.* by the authors), the resulting models which we use for our behavior will necessarily differ from the world of experience which they are models of. Thus, for us the relevant characteristic which a model will have is usefulness — that is, is the model effective for the purpose it is designed to be used for. Therefore, questions of truth, accuracy and fit with reality with respect to models of experience miss the point of modeling altogether.

Our purpose is to present a model which will be useful for the purposes of effective hypnotic communication. As with any model, the one we develop in the succeeding pages will be incomplete — specifically, there are powerful patterns of hypnotic communication in the work of Milton H. Erickson as well as in our work which we choose not to represent in the model. We have selected the patterns to be represented in our model based on our understanding of the modeling principle called elegance. Elegance is a modeling principle which states that the most highly valued model for a specific task is the one which requires the minimum number of patterns or distinctions and is still adequate for the purposes for which it is designed. Thus, in the model which follows we present the minimum number of patterns necessary for a hypnotist to communicate effectively in the context of hypnotic communication. As hypnotists, many of you will recognize many of the patterns and distinctions in this model in your own behavior. The model can be used by you to make explicit these patterns, thereby organizing your experience in a more systematic way. Patterns in your behavior which are not represented explicitly in the model can be easily integrated and essentially constitute your personal style or art. As with any learning task, you will go through a period of consciously learning to identify in your own behavior and in the behavior of your clients the patterns we present here. This is a natural stage in the process of change and learning — soon the patterns will drop out of your consciousness, achieving the status of systematic unconscious patterns of behavior, thereby leaving you free to detect still further patterns which you may find useful to incorporate into your work.[1]

Our decision to present the most elegant model — the minimal model — is also based on several other understandings which we have concerning the process of human modeling. First, what each of us as human beings detects with our sensory channels is difference.[2] One easy demonstration of this pattern is that until you finish reading this sentence you will not be conscious of the location of your left ear. The fact that you were not conscious of the location of your left ear until it was mentioned in the preceding sentence is perfectly consistent with the known patterns of human modeling. First, a conscious awareness of the location of your left ear during the task of reading this book would be an example of the lack of elegance in your program for reading. Secondly, the location of your left ear with respect to the remainder of your body has probably changed very little in the last few years. Thus, consistent with the principles of human modeling of ongoing experience, since there is no difference in the location of your left ear with respect to the remainder of your body, there is no difference to detect and thus no need to consciously represent this fact — the process of failing to represent the portions of our ongoing experience which are constant — as habituation. Habituation, then, can be understood as the process of sensing and responding unconsciously to the portion of our ongoing experience which is constant, and it applies with equal generality to the portions of our ongoing experience which are constant independently of whether those portions of our experience originate with people, are we conscious of the process of opening a door. Typically, it is only when the unconscious pattern in our behavior — that of extending our hand, grasping the door handle, and turning it — fails to yield the unconsciously anticipated result of opening the door that we become aware of any portion of our unconscious behavioral patterns of opening doors. We will refer in what follows to short sequences of behavior which are typically executed at the unconscious level of behavior as TOTEs (see *Plans and the Structure of Behavior* by G.A. Miller et al.). An example of the utilization of a TOTE in the context of hypnosis is the interruption of the standard handshake as the first step in a kinesthetically based trance induction.

For the individual described in the excerpt as well as for the reader, the standard handshake is a complex pattern of behavior which is normally carried out at the unconscious level of behavior. In other words, the handshake has the status of a single TOTE.Since the handshake is a single unit of behavior, the interruption of this single unit leaves the person interrupted momentarily without a conscious next step in behavior. Since the person whose TOTE has been interrupted is momentarily without a program, the hypnotist may suggest a next step, thereby utilizing the interruption effectively as a trance induction. In our experience, the trance state which results from the interruption of a TOTE is typically profound, and deep trance phenomena are comfortably elicited. Further if care is taken to re-orient the client to the exact position at which the interruption occurred and the remainder of the TOTE is executed, the client will have no conscious representation that anything unusual has occurred. In other words, consistent with the interrupted pattern having attained the status of a single unit of behavior at the unconscious level of behavior, any experiences which occur in the interruption can have no conscious representation unless deliberate instructions are given the client to consciously recall those experiences upon awakening.

All of the foregoing indicates that the Confusion Technique is a prolonged, highly complicated and complex procedure. Working one out and explaining the rationale of the procedure is indeed a long hard task, but once one has done that more than once, and has learned to recognize the fundamental processes involved, there can then be a very easy comfortable and rapid trance induction under some most unfavorable conditions. To illustrate this, both a spontaneous experimental instance and a clinical case will be reported. The first of these occurred at a lecture before a medical society. One of the physicians present was most interested in learning hypnosis, listened attentively during the lecture, but in the social hour preceding the lecture, he had repeatedly manifested hostile aggressive behavior toward most of his colleagues. When introduced to the author, he shook hands with a bone-crushing grip, almost jerked the author off his balance (the man was at least 6 inches taller than the author and about 65 lbs. heavier) and aggressively declared without any preamble that he would like to "see any damn fool try to hypnotize me."

When volunteers for a demonstration were requested, he came striding up and in a booming voice announced, "Well, I'm going to show everybody that you can't hypnotize me." As the man stepped up on the platform, the author slowly arose from his chair as if to greet him with a handshake. As the volunteer stretched forth his hand prepared to give the author another bone-crushing handshake, the author bent over and tied his own shoe strings slowly, elaborately and left the man standing helplessly with his arm outstretched. Bewildered, confused, completely taken aback at the author's nonpertinent behavior, at a total loss for something to do, the man was completely vulnerable to the first comprehensible communication *fitting to the situation* that was offered to him. As the second shoe string was being tied, the author said, "Just take a deep breath, sit down in that chair, close your eyes, and go deeply into a trance." After a brief casual startled reaction, my subject said, "Well I'll be damned! But how? Now do it again so I can know how you are doing it."

He was offered a choice of several traditional techniques. He chose the hand-levitation method as seeming the more interesting, and this technique was employed slowly both for his benefit and that of the audience, with another somnambulistic trance resulting.

As an experimental subject in that situation, he presented in an excellent manner the problem of adequately meeting his behavioral patterns and eliciting responsive behavior of interest primarily to the audience although he too was interested secondarily but his primary interest as a person was one diametrically opposed. He wished to elicit responses of futility from the author, but even this was a tacit acknowledgement of hypnosis as a valid phenomenon.

The explanation of what happened is rather simple. The man came up to the podium with an intense determination to do something. The author's rising as if to greet him with a handshake and then bending over to tie his shoe strings left the man standing with an outstretched hand, unable to do anything, interrupted so suddenly in the initiation of what he was going to do, too astonished by the author's completely nonpertinent behavior, utterly at a loss for something to do, and hence, completely susceptible to any clearly comprehensible suggestion of what to do fitting to the total situation that he responded relievedly to the simple quiet instruction the author offered. And of course, the man's underlying attitude toward hypnosis became manifest in his prompt request made upon his discovery of what had happened.

> Milton H. Erickson, "The Confusion Technique," in *Hypnosis*, Haley (ed.), 1967, pp. 153-154.

The third pattern in our understanding of the process of human modeling which we base our decision to present the minimal model on is the fact that consciousness is a limited phenomenon. Specifically, as humans we are limited to representing to ourselves in consciousness a small finite number of chunks of information. In his now classic paper called *The Magic Number 7∓2*, George A. Miller (1956) carefully presents the outline of the limits of consciousness. Essentially, his research leads him to the conclusion that we are capable of entertaining in consciousness 7 plus or minus 2 chunks of information. One of the most interesting implications of Miller's paper is that the size of the chunk is variable. In other words, the limitation of 7 ∓ 2 applies not to the number of bits of information, but rather to the number of chunks. Thus, by carefully selecting the code by which we organize our conscious experience, we have a great deal of latitude in increasing the amounts of bits of information we can represent to ourselves consciously. Miller is artfully vague in his discussion of what a chunk is. If we identify the term *chunk* with the notion of a pattern of behavior which has not yet achieved the status of an unconscious TOTE, then the interaction between the function of consciousness in the learning process and chunking becomes useful. As we learn to identify and respond systematically to patterning in our experience, we are able to make unconscious portions of our experience which we previously had to cope with at the level of consciousness. A chunk in consciousness is a patterning or regularity in our experience which we have not yet succeeded in making unconscious. Thus, at the beginning of the learning of a particular task, the size of the chunk will be rather small—encompassing a relatively short patterning or regularity in our experience. As this size chunk achieves the status of a TOTE — thus becoming unconscious—our consciousness is free to attend to larger level patterns which are composed of the sequencing and organizing of the TOTE's which they are composed of, or to attend to patterning in other representational systems or areas of experience.

Consider an example from your own experience. For those of you who at one time learned to ride a bicycle, remember how complex it was at first. Your first time up was overwhelming. You had to think about balancing, pushing pedals up and down, steering and watching where to steer. This was certainly more than you could handle, so perhaps your father or a friend held the rear of the bicycle so you only had to worry consciously about steering and pedaling. And if you were one of the fortunate ones who already had an unconscious program for pedaling from riding a tricycle, then the task was reduced to learning to coordinate steering and pedaling. Once these skills had been drilled into your behavior, they happened automatically, then perhaps when you weren't even looking your father let go and just ran behind and off you were, learning to coordinate the pedaling and steering with balancing. After a time you had so programmed yourself to operate the bicycle that all aspects of the task dropped outside of consciousness, leaving you free to enjoy the scenery or talk with a riding companion. No matter how long it has been since you have ridden a bike, the program will be there and if you climb on a bicycle the program will activate and you will be able to ride once again without ever thinking even for a moment about all the steps in this complex process. They are all chunked and sequenced at the unconscious level leaving you free to enjoy your ride. If they were conscious you would have to think about pedaling, steering, balancing every movement and your consciousness would be so cluttered you would either fall or run into something. The learning of patterns of behavior such as bicycle riding as unconscious programs is both useful and necessary to allow us as humans to do the varied and complex things we do every day. We would suggest that you even make this explicit as part of your learning program. For example, at the present time you are reading a book from which you can learn certain patterns of communication. If you wish to learn them thoroughly, we suggest that you take two of the patterns we will present you each day, and spend that day identifying and using that pattern all day — until it is so thoroughly practiced that you can let it drop out of consciousness and still use it systematically, thereby leaving your conscious mind free to move on to learn more patterns. You will have in essence created a TOTE for each pattern in this book. In that way you will have re-coded your experience of both hypnosis and communication. This will allow you to operate as a communicator/hypnotist as easily as you once learned to ride a bicycle.

This understanding of the notion of the relationship between chunk and TOTE allows us to apply some of the principles of modeling to the presentation of our model. For example, for effective learning to take place, the chunks or conscious patterns which we present must be of the same size in order for the re-coding process of creating TOTEs — that is, of making the patterns of effective hypnotic communication unconscious — to occur successfully. Further, in our model, we attempt to present no more than the magic number of patterns at any one level of chunking.

The Model — Primary Experience

The first notion which we introduce in the model is that of the 4-tuple. The 4-tuple is a visual representation of experience which looks like $<V, K, A_t, O>_i$

where
V = visual
K = kinesthetic
A_t = auditory tonal
O = olfactory
i = the referential index of the experiencer

the general form of the 4-tuple

$$<V, K, A_t, O>$$

The 4-tuple is a way of visually representing a person's experience at any point in time. The 4-tuple claims that for the purposes of a model of effective hypnotic communication, a person's primary experience at a moment in time can be represented adequately by a description of their visual, kinesthetic, auditory tonal and olfactory experience. A specific example may assist the reader in understanding comfortably. Assuming that you are a reader who at this point in time is sitting comfortably in a quiet place and that you are reading alone, the 4-tuple can be used to represent your present experience of the world as follows:

the specific 4-tuple which represents the reader's experience

$$\left\langle \begin{array}{cccc} \text{the printed words of,} & \text{the feeling} & , \phi , & \text{the smell of} \\ \text{the book, the} & \text{of the chair, the} & & \text{the room, the} \\ \text{lighting pattern of} & \text{temperature of} & & \text{freshness of the} \\ \text{the room} \ldots & \text{the room} \ldots & & \text{air} \ldots \end{array} \right\rangle_i$$

where i is the referential index of the reader and the blank space ϕ indicates no experience in that mode.

In words, the reader's present experience of the world is represented by a description of the visual input from the words, his present kinesthetic sensations, and the olfactory sensation available. Since, by our assumption, the reader is in a place where he is presently receiving no auditory input from the external world, the value of the variable At (the auditory tonal portion of his experience) is ϕ. The values of the V, K and O variables are specified by a description of the input from the world that is impinging on the reader at this point in time. Notice that in specifying the 4-tuple for the reader's present experience, we restricted ourselves to representing experience originating in the world external to the reader. The 4-tuple can also be used to represent the reader's total experience — that is, his present ongoing experience independently of whether it originates in the world external to the reader or not. We have found it useful in our work to identify the origin of the portion of the experience described in the 4-tuple — that is to distinguish between which portion of the experience represented by the 4-tuple originates in the world external to the person whose experience is represented by the 4-tuple and which portion is generated by the person's own internal processes. One easy way of representing this distinction is by simply attaching a superscript to each component of the 4-tuple —either an i (internally generated) or an e (externally generated). Thus assuming that the reader is reading with internal dialogue at this point in time and using the superscripts which distinguish the internally generated from externally originated components of the 4-tuple, the reader's 4-tuple would look like:

$$\left\langle \begin{array}{llll} \text{The printed words,}^e & \text{the feeling of }^e, & \text{the tempo and tonal }^i, & \text{the smell of }^e, \\ \text{of the book,} & \text{the chair, the} & \text{qualities of} & \text{the room, the} \\ \text{the lighting pattern} & \text{temperature of} & \text{the auditory} & \text{freshness of} \\ \text{in the room} \ldots & \text{the room} \ldots & \text{internal dialogue} \ldots & \text{the air} \ldots \end{array} \right\rangle_i$$

As with all the distinctions in the model, this superscript distinction between internally and externally generated experience will be employed only when it is useful for the task for which it is to be used.

The reader will notice that the superscript distinction allows the 4-tuple to be used as a way of distinguishing hallucinated or projected experience from experience originating in the external world. Erickson often discusses the difference between ordinary waking state and trance states (especially deep trance states) using the phrase *limited foci of attention*.

...Too much emphasis is placed upon external factors and the subject's responses to them. Primarily, emphasis should be placed on the intrapsychic behavior of the subject rather than upon the relationship to externalities. At best, apparatus is only an incidental aid, to be discarded at the earliest possible moment in favor of the utilization of the subject's behavior which may be initiated but not developed by the apparatus. . . The utilization of imagery rather than actual apparatus permits the subject to utilize his actual capabilities without being hampered by an adjustment to non essential externalities.

. . .the subject in a deep trance functions in accord with the unconscious understandings independently of the forces to which his conscious mind ordinarily responds; he behaves in ac -cordance with the reality which exists in the given hypnotic situation for his unconscious mind. Conceptions, memories, and ideas constitute his reality world; he is in a deep trance. The actual external environment reality with which he is surrounded is relevant only insofar as it is utilized in the hypnotic situation.

Milton H. Erickson, *Deep Trance and Its Induction*, Haley (ed.), 1967, p. 11.

In the ordinary waking state, most people are continually being distracted by experience generated either by external stimuli or by experience generated by internal stimuli. Their focus of attention is constantly shifting. Thus, one way of understanding the process of going into a deep trance is the constant focusing and riveting of consciousness on a limited number of stimuli (a general description of establishing a biofeedback loop). Since internally generated stimuli are typically more under the control of the subject (with the hypnotist's help), one powerful way to assist the client in going into a deep trance is to have them attend more and more exclusively to internal stimuli. The superscripts e and i can be used to represent the general shift of attention experienced by the client in a typical trance induction from externally originating experience to internally generated experiences, for example:

$$<V^e, K^e, A^e, O^e>_t \text{----------} > <V^i, K^i, A^e, O^e>_t \text{---------} > <V^i, K^i, A^i, O^i>_t$$

where the intermediate 4-tuple is the partial trance state where the client is attending to internally produced visual images and internally generated kinesthetic sensations to the exclusions of externally generated ones, while continuing to attend to auditory tonal (e.g. the tonal and tempo qualities of the hypnotist's voice) and olfactory experiences which originate externally.

The diligent student of hypnosis who has trained himself to

make fine sensory distinctions as he moves about in the world will recognize many responses which he sees, hears and feels in his everyday contact with people as unconscious responses and communications typical of official hypnotic trance states. Each of us uses our past experience as the basis for understanding our present experience of meeting someone new. Becoming aware that the tonal qualities of their voice, their body posture, their gestures, the melodic patterns as they speak remind us of someone else, we may find ourselves responding to them in ways which are perhaps more appropriate for the other person they remind us of. In such cases, our 4-tuple with respect to that person is a mixture of internally and externally generated experience. Such experiences indicate the power of the normally unconscious meaning making processes of communication.

In most people such unconscious mixture of internally and externally generated experience accounts for much of the difficultly they experience with people. The business man who explodes when the sales clerk at the clothing store who walks very much like his boss fails to pay attention to him and the woman who feels so small and helpless around a man whose voice tones sound so much like her father's are simply slightly exaggerated examples of the process of mixing internally and externally generated experience without making the distinction. As an effective communicator/hypnotist it will be important to understand that as each of us is responding in any communication situation, portions of our responses are to the ongoing communication and portions of our responses will be TOTEs that are more closely connected with some other time/space coordinates. For example, as children, many of us learned to detect that our parents were angry at us even before they would express it verbally by a certain look, a certain raising of an eyebrow or a certain hand gesture. We· as children created responses to these signals which as a child were useful mechanisms of coping. However, later on in life, these programs, just like the programs for riding a bicycle were still active and activatable. As hypnotist/communicators, we must be sensitive to these unconscious TOTEs: if utilized in a directed fashion, they become assets; if they are not, they can become the foundation of solid resistance. We need as communicators/hypnotists to be aware of which responses of creative responses and which are TOTES executed unconsciously and which are more appropriate for some other time/space. For example, we had a young woman who came to us for assistance. We noticed immediately that if either of us would raise an eyebrow, this woman would suddenly start apologizing and stating that she had failed to follow our instruction and that she probably wasn't smart enough to go into a trance. We noticed also that a proud smile elicited confidence and a willingness to cooperate. In the first case the 23 year old woman would speak of failure with the tonality of a teenager. In the second case she sounded more like a 5 year old. Since induction into trance is a shift from the external to the internal experience with a limited focus of attention, we both wore proud smiles and spoke to her in a childish tonality and when one of the authors began to call her *princess*, we had a completely age-regressed client. And five year olds are very easy to hypnotize.

The astute practitioner of hypnosis can come to appreciate the fascinating mixture of conscious and unconscious communication responses among people based on the mixture of internally and externally generated experience.

This leads naturally to the next distinction we introduce for the 4-tuple — that of time/space coordinates. Whenever a person generates experience internally, that experience will be based on some set of previous 4-tuples, each of which has a time/space coordinate different from the present time/space coordinate. For example, when you as a hypnotist ask your client to remember a pleasant childhood experience, you are instructing the client as to what general time/space coordinate you want on the internally generated experience you are requesting. This distinction can be represented in the 4-tuples as:

$$A_d < K^i_{t/p} \quad V^i_{t/p} \quad A^i_{t/p} \quad O^i_{t/p} >$$

where t/p subscript is the time/place coordinator of the experience the person is using as the reference structure from which he is generating his experience internally.

The internally/externally generated experience and the time/space coordinate distinctions are particularly useful in the context of psychotherapeutic techniques of change where the therapist wishes to assist the client in recovering the original experiences from the past which are preventing him from having the choices he desires in the present.

One of the most powerful learnings which we have been able to offer the people we have had the opportunity and privilege of teaching our models for communication to flow naturally from the internally/externally generated experience and the time/space coordinate distinctions we have been discussing. As communicators each of us understands the power and value of detecting, accepting and responding creatively to non-verbal or analogue messages offered to us by the people we have contact with. In the context of the work we do with our clients, the value of nonverbal communication cannot be over-emphasized. Typically our clients offer us non-verbal messages which form the basis for communication which leads to pervasive graceful change. In order to increase our skill in detecting, accepting and responding creatively to such messages, we have developed a specific communication strategy which we refer to as the up-time strategy. Each of us has a limited amount of consciousness (Miller's 7 ∓ 2 chunks). When communicating with another human being, if we choose to bring into consciousness some portion of our past — some internally generated portion of experience from another time/space coordinate — we consequently lose some portion of our sensory contact with that person. When we lose some portion of our sensory contact during communication with a client, we will fail to detect nonverbal messages which are constantly being offered (typically at the unconscious level of communication) from that person. Our experience is that such messages are the very basis for assisting that person in rapid and profound change. The up-time strategy is simply the process of organizing our communication in such a way that we use all of our consciousness on sensory experience. In other words, a communicator using an up-time strategy has an ongoing 4-tuple in which all of the superscripts are $e._s$

Language — Secondary Experience

The next distinction which we introduce into the model is that of language. Specifically, we represent the relationship between a language representation and the experience it represents as:

$$A_d \langle \ V, K, A_t, O \rangle$$

where A_d = auditory digital (language)

This relationship we refer to as a Complex Equivalence. In other words, a Complex Equivalence is the relationship between a language representation and the 4-tuple or set of 4-tuples which the language represents — the relationship between a word and the set of experiences it represents. For example, in doing experimental work in hypnosis, greater depth with greater speed in our experience results when the hypnotist gets a Complex Equivalence for the nominalization "deep trance" or even for that matter "trance". A 4-tuple description of what the client expects his experience to be in trance will aid the hypnotist in knowing what kind of suggestions to give and also in clearing up misunderstandings about the word *trance.*Some clients answer the question, "How would you know if you were in a trance? with the response that they would have no internal dialogue. Others claim they would see no internal visual images, and still others say they would just feel totally relaxed. The process of getting a full complex equivalence (all variables of the 4-tuple considered) will aid the hypnotist greatly in knowing how to create an experience which will count as an experience of trance, thereby aiding the client in having confidence that he or she is a competent hypnotic subject.

As a specific example, consider the 4-tuple(s) accessed by the word "fire".

fire

$$\left\langle \begin{array}{llll} \text{the sight of ,} & \text{the feeling of ,} & \text{the sounds of ,} & \text{the smell of} \\ \text{flickering flames,} & \text{heat, the choking} & \text{crackling flames} & \text{the smoke and} \\ \text{of smoke, ...} & \text{sensation of smoke} & \text{and burning material, ...} & \text{burning materials, ...} \\ & \text{in lungs, ...} & & \end{array} \right\rangle$$

The particular value of the variables of the 4-tuple(s) which correspond to the language representation "fire" are fairly consistent from person to person in this culture. Thus, we find a great deal of agreement about the Complex Equivalence of which 4-tuple(s) correspond to the word "fire". Such wide-spread and consistent correspondences make language effective as a communication device. The 4-tuple(s) which each of us access for certain other words and phrases are, however, much less consistent. Imagine, for example, the variation in the values of the variables of the 4-tuples which each of us would assign to words such as *love, justice, equality*. These words — all nominalizations — are so variable in the 4-tuples which they access that mis-communication is the rule rather than the exception.

A major portion of the task of language learning which each of us experienced as children was the assignment of phonological sequences (the sounds in the language we learned) to the 4-tuples of our experience. This assignment of sound to 4-tuple is one of the most pervasive ways in which a language system influences (at the most unconscious level of behavior) our experiences of the world. By selecting specific 4-tuples and sets of 4-tuples out of all the 4-tuples which we experience and assigning them a name, the language both assists us in identifying the patterns which the users of the language have found important in organizing their experience and simultaneously draws our attention away from the other 4-tuples and sets of 4-tuples which have not yet been coded into a language representation.[6]

We have chosen to visually represent the language portion of experience as an operator on the 4-tuple distinct from the basic variables of experience. Our choice here is based on several lines of evidence. First, language is of a different logical level of experience — any portion of the 4-tuple may be translated into a language representation but not vice versa. Specifically, the language system, a digital system, includes the possiblity of expressing negation and tense while analogue system of communication do not have these possibilities. (see Bateson, 1972 for discussion) This is the map-territory distinction. Secondly, the language system is acquired by us at a later time than our ability to experience the world visually, kinesthetically, auditory tonally, and by the sense of smell. The usefulness of this distinction in the organizing your experience in hypnosis must, of course, be the justification for its representation in the model.

One minimal use of this distinction lies in the fact that most of the clients who come to us as therapists are there because they have, in the first place, mistaken the map (language) for the territory (experience). They ask the hypnotist for what they want in language. Typically the language description is so far removed from the experience they want, that they have no idea whether or not they have the resources available to get what it is they desire. Several clients will come in and state that they desire a greater sense of confidence. *Confidence* is a language representation of some experience the client desires. Just what exactly that experience is the therapist has no way of knowing until he reconnects the language description with experience. *Confidence* for the one client will be a specific set of body sensations; for another, it will be a certain image (internal) of himself and for still others, it will be different yet.'[7]

Representational System — The R-Operator on the 4-Tuple

The research done by George A. Miller applies with equal force to the hypnotist in the context of the hypnotic encounter and to each of us in our everyday experience of the world — in other words, there is much which we sense, much that we receive as input from the external world which we do not represent to ourselves in consciousness. For example, until the reader read the above description of the specified 4-tuples, it is likely that he was unaware of the feeling of the chair, the temperature of the room...The point we are making here is that the process of consciously attending to sensations— what we call consciousness in our experience— is only a small portion of the sensations available to us. The distinction between what we represent consciously and what we are sensing as a total organism can usefully be represented by defining an operator on the 4-tuple as follows:

$$R \ \langle V, K, A_t, O \rangle \ \text{--------->} \ \langle V, 0, 0, 0 \rangle$$

In words, then, the application of the operator to the 4-tuple which represents the organism's total experience yields the portion of the experience available in the organism's consciousness. The reader will recognize that the result of the application of R to the 4-tuple yields what we refer to in *Patterns I* as the client's most highly valued representational system. The above example, then, represents a person who is attending solely to the visual component of the total experience — the person who typically attends primarily to what they see. Thus for a person whose most highly valued representational system is kinesthetic, the application of the operator R would yield a different outcome, namely:

$$R \ \langle V, K, A_t, O \rangle \ \text{------->} \ \langle 0, K, 0, 0 \rangle$$

This operator creates an explicit representation for the notion of most highly valued representational system — specifically, the person's most highly valued representational system is the variable in the 4-tuple which has a non-null value after the R operator has been applied to the 4-tuple which represents the person's total experience. Notice that this is independent of whether the value of that variable originates in the world external to the person or is the result of some internal process. In general, the person's most highly valued representational system will coincide with portions of the external world which they are aware of — knowing this is of great importance in understanding how to communicate effectively with a client in the hypnotic encounter.

In addition to the use of the R operator on the 4-tuple, we shall also use the R operator on the A_d (the language representation) plus the associated 4-tuple(s). For example, the application of the R operator to the following expression is possible.

R (fire

| the sight of, flickering flames, of smoke, . . . | the feeling , of heat, the choking sensations of smoke in lungs, . . . | the sounds of , the crackling of flames and material, . . . | the smell of smoke and burning materials, . . . |

This allows us to represent the situation in which the person whose conscious experience is being represented is aware of the sound of someone shouting the word "fire" for example. Thus the R operator can be applied either directly to the 4-tuple or to the representation of the pattern called Complex Equivalence — that is, the language representation plus the associated 4-tuples(s).[9]

Let us review the 4-tuple model presented thus far. Its main purpose is to give the hypnotist a tool to organize both his experience and his techniques in a way that will give him greater fluidity and proficiency in the hypnotic encounter. The 4-tuple basically has the following dimensions. Experience at any point in time will have (though not in consciousness) at least some visual (internal or external) some kinesthetic (internal or external) some auditory tonal (internal or external) and some olfactory (internal or external) dimension which originates at some time/space coordinates. Each of these combined at any point in time into a 4-tuple can be assigned an auditory digital (language) representation.

The A_d is an operator which is the name of any specific 4-tuple. An R operator can also be applied and represents those portions of the 4-tuple the client is aware of. The R operator, in essence, describes, what consciousness is at any time for any specific client. Now is the time to take the model and make it a practical tool for hypnosis.

General Discussion of the Use of the R-Operator and 4-Tuple in Hypnotic Inductions

In Volume I of the *Patterns* series, the process of hypnotic induction was described in terms of pacing and leading. The advanced student of hypnosis and communication will find it useful to understand these processes in terms of the R operator over the 4-tuple. Let us begin with the notion of pacing. Essentially, pacing is the process by which the hypnotist makes contact with the client, or in terms of Patterns I, the hypnotist meets the client at the client's model of the world. Overt pacing usually involves the hynotist's offering verbalizations which match some portion of the client's ongoing experience. Covert pacing, a very powerful induction technique will be considered later in the section on meaningful communication with an incongruent client — the so-called "resistant client".

In traditional ritualistic verbal hypnotic inductions, the hypnotist offers a series of suggestions verbally which represent to the client in language some portion of their ongoing experience. As the client hears the hypnotist's verbalizations, he checks his experience to determine whether or not the verbalizations by the hypnotist are, in fact, an accurate representation of his ongoing experience. Once this verified biofeedback loop has been accomplished, the hypnotist may come to link the pacing verbalizations with leading verbalizations to lead the client into an altered state for the purposes of the hypnotic encounter (see Patterns, volume I, pages 15-20, 137-152, 209-215 for details of the linking techniques). Much of the more graceful aspects of the traditional ritualistic verbal hypnotic induction can be understood in terms of the R-operator on the 4-tuple. If the hypnotist has the ability to detect what specific portion of experience the client has access to, then he knows precisely which set of pacing statements will be an immediate effective pace for the client at that point in time. Thus, for example, if a client offers a series of statements which include phrases such as:

> I *feel* I would benefit greatly . . .
> I want to *get in touch* with some . . .
> You are a *warm* person . . .
> So many people are *insensitive* and *callous* . . .

the hypnotist detects that the client is attending primarily in consciousness to the kinesthetic portions of his experience. Thus, when beginning his induction the hypnotist will offer a series of suggestions which presupposes a kinesthetic representational system. Since the client has access to those portions of experience, he will immediately be able to verify that the hypnotist's verbalizations are accurate for his ongoing experience. In terms of the R operator on the 4-tuple, the hypnotist understands that the client's experience can be represented as follows:

$$R \ (A_d < K, \ V, \ A_t, \ O >) \longrightarrow K$$

Consequently, the hypnotist, in order to establish an effective pace with this client, will select verbalizations which use kinesthetic predicates. A hypnotist who fails to make the representational system distinction and who offers suggestions to assist the client in developing internal visual images will frequently find himself with a confused and possibly a resistant client. Once the representational system distinction is made by the hypnotist, such mis-communication is easily and comfortably avoided.

This initial movement, common in our experience to all successful communication whether for the purposes of hypnosis or not — the meeting of the client at the client's model of the world — insures that the hypnotist has tuned him or herself to the client adequately. Once this initial biofeedback loop is established, the hypnotist can display some of his or her creativity. As we have mentioned, even within the representational system which each of us selects at a moment in time as primary, there are an infinite number of experiences available which lie outside the bounds of our rather limited consciousness. By offering a series of pacing verbalizations within the representational system of the client but outside their usual awareness, the hypnotist can gracefully lead the client to new experiences. Erickson presents several excellent examples of the employment of pacing verbalizations based on the representational system distinction in his superb article *Further Techniques of Hypnosis — Utilization Techniques.* Note as you read through these that Erickson seizes upon the information offered by the client as to which portion of the world of ongoing experience is available to them and utilizes the representational system information by directing their attention to experiences within that representational system but outside of the client's present awareness. In both of the cases cited, Erickson notes that the visual dimension of ongoing experience is the relevant representational system to establish contact in, and he immediately utilizes by offering pacing verbalizations in that system.

There are patients who prove unresponsive and resistant to the usual induction techniques, who are actually readily amenable to hypnosis. They are encountered more frequently in the psychotherapeutic practice but are also seen in general medical and dental practice and judged to often be unsuited to the use of hypnosis. These patients are those who are unwilling to accept any suggested behavior until after their own resistant, contradictory or opposing behavior has first been met by the operator. By reason of their physical condition, anxiety, intense interest, concern or absorption in their own behavior, they are unable to cooperate actively or passively to permit an effective alteration of it. For these patients, what may be termed *Techniques of Utilization* frequently serve to meet most adequately their special needs. These same techniques serve to facilitate in both rapidity and ease the process of trance induction in the average patient. They are, in essence, no more than a simple reversal of the usual procedure of inducting hypnosis. Ordinarily, trance induction is based upon securing from the patient some form of initial acceptance and cooperation with the operator. In Techniques of Utilization, the usual procedure is reversed: There is an initial acceptance of, and a ready cooperation with, the patient's presenting behavior by the operator, however seemingly adverse it may appear to be in the clinical situation.

These various Techniques of Utilization will be clarified and illustrated by the following clinical examples:

Example 1: This patient entered the office in a most energetic fashion and declared at once that he did not know if he was hypnotizable. He was willing to go into a trance if it were at all possible, provided the writer would approach the entire matter in an intellectual fashion rather than in a mystical, ritualistic manner. He declared that he needed psychotherapy for a variety of reasons and that he had tried various schools of psychotherapy extensively without benefit. Hypnosis had been attempted on various occasions and had failed miserably because of "mysticism" and "a lack of appreciation for the intellectual approach."

Inquiry elicited that he felt an "intelligent" approach signified, not a suggestion of ideas, but questioning him concerning his own thinking and feeling in relation to reality. The writer, he declared, should recognize that he was sitting in a chair, that the chair was in front of a desk, and that these constituted absolute facts of reality. As such, they could not be overlooked, forgotten, denied or ignored. In further illustration, he pointed out that he was obviously tense, anxious and concerned about the tension tremors of his hands which were resting on the arms of the chair, and that he was also highly distractable, noticing everything about him.

The writer immediately seized upon this last comment as the basis for the initial cooperation with him. He was told, "Please proceed with an account of your ideas and understanding, permitting me only enough interruptions to *ensure that I understand fully and that I follow along with you.* For example, you mentioned the chair but obviously you have seen my desk and have been distracted by the objects on it. Please explain fully.

He responded verbosely with a wealth of more or less connected comments about everything in sight. At every slight pause, the writer interjected a word or phrase to direct his attention anew. These interruptions, made with increasing frequency, were as follows: "And that paperweight; the filing cabinet; the pictures on the wall; the changing focus of your eyes as you glance about; the interest of the book titles; the tension in your shoulders; the feeling of the chair; the disturbing noises and thoughts; weight of hands and feet; weight of problems, weight of desk; the stationery stand; the records of many patients; the phenomena of life, of illness, of emotion, of physical and mental behavior; the restfulness of relaxation; the need to attend to one's needs; the need to attend to one's tension while looking at the desk or the paperweight or the filing cabinet; the comfort of withdrawal from the environment; fatigue and its development; the unchanging character of the desk; the monotony of the filing cabinet; the need to take a rest; the comfort of closing one's eyes; the relaxing sensation of a deep breath; the delight of learning passively; the capacity for intellectual learning by the unconscious." Various other similar brief interjections were offered, slowly at first and then with increasing frequency.

Initially, these interjections were merely supplementary to the patient's own train of thought and utterances. At first, the effect was simply to stimulate him to further effort. As this response was made, it became possible to utilize his acceptance of stimulation of his behavior by a procedure of pausing and hesitating in the completion of an interjection. This served to effect in him an expectant dependency upon the writer for further and more complete stimulation.

As this procedure was continued, gradually and unnoticed by the patient, his attention was progressively directed in inner subjective experiential matters. It then became possible to use almost directly a simple, progressive relaxation technique of trance induction and to secure a light medium trance.

Throughout therapy, further trance inductions were basically comparable, although the procedure became progressively abbreviated.

Example 2. Comparable to the first patient was the woman who presented a somewhat similar problem. She stated that, in all previous attempts to secure therapy, she had been defeated in her efforts by a compulsive attentiveness to the minutiae of the immediate environment. She invariably had difficulty in completing her history and in attending to what was said to her because of an overpowering need to attend and to comment upon what she saw about her. (Even this small amount of history was interrupted by her inquiries about or simple mention of various objects in the office.) A psychiatrist and a family friend had suggested that hypnosis might enable her to cooperate in therapy and had referred her to the writer.

Since she had impressed the writer as a possible candidate

for hypnotherapy and because little progress was being made in the interview, hypnosis was attempted by utilizing her own behavior in the following fashion:

As she inquired about a paperweight on the desk, reply was quickly made, "It is on the corner of the desk just behind the clock." As she flicked her gaze to the clock and asked urgently, "What time is it?" she was answered with, "The minute hand indicates the same numeral as does the desk calendar."

There followed a whole series of comments and inquiries by her without pause for any replies and with a rapid shifting from one object or subject to another. Her behavior was similar to that of an unhappy small child, warding off questioning by directing the interrogation into irrelevant, distracting avenues.

It was not possible to interrupt her verbal flow except with difficulty, and then fruitlessly. However, the measure of extending a paper knife compelled her to make mention of it. As she responded and then continued in her monologue, the writer polished his glasses, again forcing her to make a comment in accord with her pattern of behavior. Next she was interrupted by a placing of the glasses in their case; then the desk blotter was shifted, a glance was directed at the bookcase, and the schedule book opened and closed.

Each of these acts was fitted by her into her compulsive stream of utterances. At first, these various acts were performed by the writer at intervals and rather quickly. As she developed an attitude of expectation for the writer's silent interruptions, his movements were deliberately slowed and made with slight hesitant pauses. This compelled her to slow her own behavior and to await the writer's utilization of her conduct. Then the writer added to his silent indication of objects an identifying word or phrase of comment.

This continued procedure had a progressively profound inhibitory effect upon her, so that she began to depend more and more exclusively upon the writer to indicate either verbally or by gesture the next object she was to comment upon or to name. After about 40 minutes of this, it became possible to instruct her to close her eyes and to name from memory everything that she had seen and to do this until she developed a deep hypnotic sleep. As she obeyed, she was prompted, "And now, 'paperweight' and deeper asleep; and now 'clock,' go even deeper into the trance." etc., until in another 10 minutes, a profound somnambulistic trance state was secured.

Thereafter, through this measure of utilizing as an induction technique her own pattern of resistant behavior, ready cooperation in therapy marked the clinical course of this previously "impossible" patient. Initially, each therapeutic session began her compulsive behavior which was immediately utilized for the induction of another therapeutic trance. Later, a simple gesture indicating the chair in which she was to sit sufficed to elicit a trance state.

> Milton H. Erickson, *Further Techniques of Hypnosis—Utilization Techniques*, Haley (ed.), 1967, pp. 32-34.

In the visual representation — the 4-tuple and the R operator — we are developing here, Erickson understands that for both of these clients

$$R \; (A_d < K, \; V, \; O, \; A_t >) \text{----------} > V^e$$

Thus, his effective and graceful induction begins with a series of pacing verbalizations directing the client to more and more experiences within the representational system available to them. There are two additional comments of use derived from these examples. Note first that the suggestions Erickson offers lead systematically from experiences with an *e* superscript (experiences externally generated) to experiences with an *i* superscript (experiences internally generated). Secondly, both these examples demonstrate a second major way in shich the R-operator is useful in the hypnotist's organizing his behavior in the context of hypnotic inductions.

As Erickson establishes an effective pace within the clients' own representational system, he begins to shift from their representational system to another variable in the 4-tuple. He does this specifically by what we refer to as the principle of representational system overlap. (See *The Structure of Magic*, volume II, page 24 for more discussion.) More specifically, this principle states that once an effective pace is established within the client's own representational system, the hypnotist may begin to lead the client to an altered state of consciousness by finding the point of overlap between some experience in that representational system and that same experience in one of the associated representational system not normally a part of the client's ongoing experience. For example, when working with a client who is capable of detailed internal visual imagery and with whom an adequate pace has been established, we created a vivid, rich, detailed image of a forest of trees. Once this visual image is focused, we call the client's attention to the fact that he can see the trees swaying, their branches moving gracefully, and then to the fact that,

> "...as you watch those trees swaying in the wind,
> enjoy the sound of the wind rushing through the trees..."

Once we receive verification from the client that he is hearing the sound of the wind rushing through the trees (typically by the unconscious head movements or one of the accessing cues typical of an auditory internal experience), we may choose to extend the experience into another of the variables of the 4-tuple,

> "...now the sound of the wind rushing through those trees as you watch them sway is quite pleasant,...as pleasant for many people as the refreshing feeling of coolness as the wind blows on your face,... and through your hair..."

> ...breezes which carry the warm pungent odors of fresh-cut grass on a warm summer afternoon..."

This powerful maneuver can be easily represented in terms of the 4-tuple and the R-operator as :

$$R_{time_1} \quad (A_d < V, K, A_t, O >) ----->A_d^e \ \& \ V^i$$

(seeing the trees)

$$R_{time_2} \quad (A_d < V, K, A_t, O >) ----->A_d^e \ \& \ V^i \ \& \ A_t^i$$

(hearing the wind)

$$R_{time_3} \quad (A_d < V, K, A_t, O >) ----->A_d^e \ \& \ V^i \ \& \ A_t^i \ \& \ K^i$$

(feeling the air)

$$R_{time_4} \quad (A_d < V, K, A_t, O >) ----->A_d^e \ \& \ V^i \ \& \ A_t^i \ \& \ K^i \ \& \ O^i$$

(smelling the odors)

Notice that the client's 4-tuple after this maneuver is one which is composed entirely of variables with i superscript; the only e superscript belonging to the A_d^e variable — in this case the hypnotist's words.

$$A_d^e < V^i, K^i, A_t^i, O^i >$$

A close examination of the Erickson examples will reveal precisely the same principle. For example, in the first case cited, Erickson begins by directing the client's attention to various objects in his visual field such as ...*the desk*...*the objects on the desk*...*the paperweight*...*the filing cabinet*...Next Erickson directs the client's attention to a special class of objects in the client's visual field — specifically, parts of the client's body which he can see: *your foot on the rug*...*your right hand on the arm of the chair*...Next Erickson overlaps representational systems from V into K:...*the changing focus of your eyes as you glance about*...*the tension in your shoulders*...*the feeling of the chair*...

The two principles concerning the utilization of the R-operator in hypnotic inductions we have been discussing presuppose the hypnotist's ability to detect what the client's representational system is. We present specific ways in which you can train yourself to detect your client's representational system so as to respond creatively by utilizing that information.

When each of us selects the words we use to communicate to one another verbally, we typically select those words at the unconscious level of functioning. These words, then, indicate which portions of the world of internally and externally available experience we have access to at that moment in time. More specifically, the set of words known as predicates (verbs, adjectives and adverbs) are particularly indicative. Secondly, each of us has developed particular body movements which indicate to the astute observer which representational system we are using. Especially rich in significance are the eye scanning patterns which we have developed. Thus, for the student of hypnosis, predicates in the verbal system and eye scanning patterns in the nonverbal system offer quick and powerful ways of determining which of the potential meaning making resources — the representational systems — the client is using at a moment in time, and therefore how to respond creatively to the client. Consider, for example, how many times you have asked someone a question and they have paused, said:"Hmmmmm, let's see" and accompanying this verbalization, they move their eyes up and to the left. Movement of the eyes up and to the left stimulates (in right handed people) eidetic images located in the non dominant hemisphere. The neurological pathways that come from the left side of both eyes (left visual fields) are represented in the right cerebral hemisphere (non dominant). The eye scanning movement up and to the left is a common way people use to stimulate that hemisphere as a method for accessing visual memory. Eye movements up and to the right conversely stimulate the left cerebral hemisphere and constructed images — that is, visual representations of things that the person has never seen before (see *Patterns*, volume I, page 182).

Developing your skill in detecting the client's most highly valued representational system will give you access to an extremely powerful utilization tool for effective hypnotic communication. There are two principal ways which we have found effective in teaching people in our training seminars to refine their ability to detect representational systems.

(1) attending to accessing clues which may be detected visually. Specifically (for the right handed person):

accessing cue	representational system indicated	
eyes up and to the left...	eidetic imagery	(V)
eyes up and to the right...	constructed imagery	(V)
eyes defocused in position...	imagery	(V)
eyes down and to the left...	auditory internal	(A)
telephone postures...	auditory internal	(A)
eyes left or right, same level of gaze...	auditory internal	(A)
eyes down and to the right...	kinesthetics	(K)

(2) attending to the choice of predicates selected (typically, unconsciously) by the client to describe his experience (see *Patterns*, volume I, pages 68-76, 82-86, and *The Structure of Magic*, volume II, part I). When describing experiences, each of us selects words to describe the portions of experience we attend most closely to. Thus, as communicators, when we train ourselves to detect which representational system is presupposed by the words selected by our clients to describe their experience, we have information which we can utilize effectively in our communication with them.

These are, of course, only two ways of learning to detect representational systems — there are many others. We have found, for example, that breathing patterns are an excellent indicator of which representational system a person is using at a point in time to organize and represent their experience to themselves. During visualization, for example, the person's breathing tends to become shallow and high in the chest. Other equally useful indicators in our experience are the shifts in the tonal qualities of the person's voice, the tempo of speech, the color of the person's skin...We have presented two specific ways of detecting representational systems in sufficient detail to allow the reader to train him or herself to detect the representational system being used by a client at a point in time. Once you have comfortably mastered these two techniques — refined your ability to make these sensory distinctions — we suggest that you explore for yourselves other indicators which allow you to gain the same information. Such exercises in making sensory distinctions will not only increase your ability to be effective and graceful in your hypnotic communication but will increase and refine your ability to have the sensory experience which is, in our experience, the very foundation of effective communication and hypnosis.

With this in mind, we offer the following exercise: select a specific set of clients and spend the first 5 to 10 minutes in the session with them asking questions which will, by presupposition, direct their attention to the various representational sytems. For example, if I were to ask you how many words there are in the title of this book, there are a number of ways you could access and represent to yourself that information. You might visualize (V^i) the cover of the book and literally count the words; you might say the title of the book to yourself and keep count of the number of the words with finger movements (K). If, however, I were to ask you whether the color of the letters in the title of the book were the same colors as the letters in the authors' names, I have presupposed by use of the predicated *color* in my request that you will access and represent visually. Thus, by a judicious choice of predicates, I can direct your attention to one or another of the representational systems. This is of particular value to the reader who is interested in having these tools available to him or herself. By systematically selecting the predicates you use in asking questions, you can reduce the complexity of the communications to a point where you can easily learn to detect the accessing cues being offered to you non-verbally as the client attempts to respond to your questions. This simple exercise will in a very short period of time tune you to making the sensory distinctions necessary for the powerful utilization of representational systems. In addition, by asking such directed questions at the beginning of a session, you are systematically accessing the very resources within the clients which will form the foundation to make the change he or she desires. Below are listed some sample questions with associated typical responses you may easily detect — we recommend that you adjust the content of the questions to whatever is appropriate to your situation.

Eidetic images:
>   What color are your mother's eyes?
>   What color is your car?
>   Where did you first see me?
>   People will typically look up and left, some will also use tonal access (tonal distinctions are also mediated by the non-dominate hemisphere). Some people who are extremely fast at visualizing

won't look up to the left, they will simply defocus their eyes slightly in position., make an image and then re-focus.

Constructed Imagery:
>Can you imagine a purple cow?
>What color should I paint my House?
>Can you see yourself forty pounds lighter?

Typically people will look up and right with slight variation from person to person.

Kinesthetic:
>Have you ever felt really alert?
>Does your right hand feel warmer than your left?
>Do you feel more comfortable now than when you first arrived?

Typically people will shift their gaze down and to the right, and when you ask a question like "how do you feel about feeling depressed" people will typically touch themselves somewhere on their body if they're responsing kinesthetically.

Auditory:
>When was the first time you heard me say your name?
>Can you say (any sentence) inside your head?
>Can you hear music in your head?
>How do you know when you have internal dialogue?

The most commonly occurring auditory internal positions: postures where the persom is making contact with his hand and the side of his head; usually his temple area— the hand position is highly variable and can be used effectively to understand something of the kind of auditory internal which is occurring (e.g. index finger extended). In terms of eye scanning patterns, the client who is accessing auditory internal will typically glance slighly down and to the left, or to either side at the same level of eye fixation as obtained prior to beginning accessing: all three of these cases of eye scanning cues, the person's eyes are typically defocused. Often accompanying these accessing cues, you will notice a tendency for the person to cock his or her head as though presenting one or another ear.

Lead System — The L-Operator on the 4-Tuple

It is our understanding that at any moment in time there is an infinitely rich set of experience available to each of us as humans. These experiences may derive wholly from external sources (the e superscript on the 4-tuple) or wholly from internally generated experience (the i superscript on the 4-tuple), or may be some interesting mixture of the two. As we discussed previously, out of this constantly fluctuating world of experience, we select (usually unconsciously) some portion which we become aware of — the R operator on the 4-tuple. Our experience leads us to believe that although only a small portion of our ongoing experience is available to us at a moment in time, the information coming in through our sensory channels is being processed and represented at the unconscious level of functioning. Parallelly, our experience has indicated that, with the possible exception of organic insult to the nervous system, at any moment in time, each of us is engaging unconsciously all of the representational systems which we have presented here. Thus what we have been calling a person's representational system is simply the portion of the complex and integrated cognitive processes being used which is accessed into consciousness.

This way of understanding the complex processes each of us use to create the maps or models we guide our behavior with, makes available a distinction which we have found to be extremely powerful in our therapeutic work. Since consciousness is a limited phenomenon, the situation could logically arise where the representational system which a person uses to access/organize their experience is different than the representational system which they use to bring the information into consciousness. For example, if I were to ask you which of the doors in your house sounds the loudest when slammed, you might respond by first accessing visually (V) each of the doors in your house, then perhaps you would make some implicit muscle movement (K) corresponding to the movement of slamming the doors, and finally, you would compare the sounds (A_t)of each of the slammed doors and respond verbally (A_d). Now, if the initial systems you used (either the V or K) had occurred without entering your consciousness, there would have been a difference between the system you use to access with (your lead system) and the system you use to bring the information requested into consciousness. Thus we make a distinction between the system the client initially uses to access the information requested and the system he uses to bring the information into consciousness: the first, the one used to access, we call the lead system; the second, the system used to represent the information in consciousness, we will continue to refer to as the representational system — the client's R operator. In terms of the exercise we presented previously (Exercise A), the predicates that a person uses will identify the representational system (the R operator) while the accessing cues will identify the lead system (the L operator).

In the visual representation for the 4-tuple we have been developing, we can easily define a new operator over the 4-tuple — the L operator which identifies the client's lead system:

$$L < A_t, \ O, \ V, \ K > \text{---------} > (V)$$

It follows then, quite naturally, that the case where there is a split between a person's lead and representational system can be represented visually as the case where the R-operator and the L-operator across the 4-tuple yield different outcomes:

$$R < A_t, \ O, \ V, \ K > \text{---------} > (X)$$

$$L < A_t, \ O, \ V, \ K > \text{---------} > (Y)$$

where $X \neq Y$

Perhaps several examples from the reader's experience will assist in making the distinction clearer. One of the most frequent examples of a situation in which many people have a distinction between their lead system and their representational system is the experience called *jealousy*. Typically, when a person is jealous and cannot "get control over their feelings," they are making visual images and/or auditory internal tape loops about what could be happening between the person they are jealous of and someone else. They then become aware of feeling angry, sad, uncomfortable or whatever feeling would be appropriate if what they are imaging and/or hearing internally were occurring right before them. Thus the visual and/or auditory portions of their experience generated internally lead their K system or feelings. When those visual images and/or auditory internal tape loops are outside of consciousness, they are aware only of the feelings, and typically have great difficulty coping as they have no idea where the feelings are coming from or how to response to as to have some choice in the matter (see fuzzy functions, part III, *The Structure of Magic*, volume II for further discussion).

Many therapists and hypnotists we have had the privilege of training mention early in their contact with us that many of the distinctions which we offer in our models "make sense" out of some of the intuitions which they have developed and found useful in their work. Upon exploring those intuitions with them, the typical result is that they have learned to detect minimal cues visually and auditorially (especially, A_t — the tonal and tempo portion of the A system) which they represent as body sensations. They know by the "feel of things" when a client is ready for some particular change, or when they are being incongruent or when the session has reached a natural finishing point or when the client has some "unfinished business". This is another example of the distinction between lead and representational system. These therapists and hypnotists are leading with their ability to make fine visual and auditory distinctions unconsciously and are representing the result of making those unconscious sensory distinctions in their K systems in consciousness.

The situation so frequently encountered in psychotherapeutic uses of hypnosis or with so-called "impossible" clients who desire hypnosis in conjunction with dental or medical work but do not respond appropriately to the more ritualistic approaches to hypnosis —the situation where there is a difference between lead system and representational system — can be usefully understood as a special case of incongruity. Specifically, it is the failure to match representational system and lead system. This form of incongruity is particularly powerful as it is a form incongruity — as opposed to a content incongruity. The actual patterns of making meaning are involved in the incongruity. As with all of the patterns we have presented, there is nothing inherently positive or negative about organizing your experience with fuzzy functions. In the context both of the psychotherapeutic applications of hypnosis and with "impossible" clients in the dental and medical applications of hypnosis, checking to determine whether there is a match or mismatch between the client's lead and representational system will yield important information as to how to usefully proceed effectively and creatively with such clients.

In terms of the hypnotist's response to clients who have a split between their lead system and their representational system, typically assisting them in having the choice both of bringing any system they choose into consciousness and using any system as lead resolves not only the specific "problem" they come to us for help with, but gives them choices which allows them to make pervasive change in any content area of their lives they choose. More limited therapeutic goals involve arranging for signals from representational systems outside of consciousness to the client's representational system (the one in consciousness) so that the client comes to have some choice regarding the "problem" involved. When you as a hypnotist encounter the situation where there is a distinction between the client's lead and representational system, there are a number of powerful ways to utilize this situation. One very dramatic choice is to mark analogically in the lead system; thereby passing instructions to the lead unconscious system for the purposes of, say, inducing a profound trance. Since the messages analogically presented are directed to the lead system which is outside of consciousness for such clients, their unconscious response is immediate and profound, and, of course, they have no consciousness of what has occurred. Such is the stuff from which what has traditionally been called magic is created.

We present a transcript of a client seen by the authors which includes some of the relevant procedures for detecting and utilizing representational systems and lead systems.

Transcript

Lindsey, a young woman about 26 years of age, enters the offices and nervously sits down.

Hypnotist: Are you Lindsey?

Lindsey:(eyes move up and to the left) yes

Hypnotist: What can I do for you?

Lindsey: (eyes again move up and to the left) umm let's see...A...I...well...(head nods up and down) I was hoping that hypnosis could help me to be...un (eyes go up and to the left again) not be depressed all the time, (Lindsey looks quickly at the hypnotists) Is that stupid?

Hypnotist: (slowly moving his head back and forth no) Yes, in a way there is no way I can help you not to be depressed but at the same time hypnosis can help you.

Lindsey: (sighing with relief, looks up and to the left) I just feel (places her hands on her chest at the midline and looks at the hypnotist) I just feel down most of the time and I don't know why. I went for therapy and it just didn't help I don't...

Hypnotist: How do you know when you're depressed?

Lindsey: (looks up and to the left) I just feel (places her hands on her chest at the midline...

In just this short excerpt, the hypnotist has enough information to discern a tremendous amount about Lindsey.

$$(R < V, K, A_t, O > \text{---------}>(V^e)$$

$$(R < V, K, A_t, O > \text{---------}> K^i)$$

Lindsey, in the example, is typically either aware of kinesthetic internal or visual external. Changing her consciousness implies shifting her consciousness to experiences normally outside these realms. We also know that for Lindsey the kinesthetic internal experiences themselves are derived from visual internal processes — that she experiences body sensations which are appropriate for the internally generated visual images. When asked how does she know she is depressed, she first looks up and to the left and then says she just feels depressed. The acute observer will become aware that this is a common pattern in the clients who come in for therapy. Such clients are running some internal process outside of consciousness and also typically out of control. Lindsey, for example in this case, turns out to be visualizing herself being alone, bored...She is unaware of this visualization process — she is only aware of the negative feelings she described as depression. Thus, Lindsey presents an excellent examples of the distinction between a person's lead sytem and their representational system.

The trance work used with Lindsey proceeded in the following way. First, altering Lindsey's consciousness would first mean shifting her from the processing strategies she was operating out of to some altered state of consciousness which would allow her to exercise some control over the "problem" she needs assistance with. Since her difficulty revolves around a fuzzy function involving her generating internal visual images outside of consciousness and then experiencing kinesthetically the feelings which are appropriately associated with those internally generated visual images, there are two altered states which would be of immediate obvious assistance in her gaining some control over her "problem: either,

$$R < V, K, A_t, O > \ \text{---------} > (K^e)$$

or

$$R < V, K, A_t, O > \ \text{---------} > (V^i)$$

In words, if Lindsay learns to alter her consciousness in a way which allows her either to attend in consciousness to kinesthetic sensations externally generated (K^e) or to visual images internally generated (V^i), then she will have effectively broken the fuzzy function which generates her "problem". Specifically, these two choices represent Lindsay gaining control over her own processes either by attending to her actual kinesthetic contact with the world (for example, the feeling of the chair, the freshness of the air on her face, the warmth where her right leg is crossed over her left...) or by bringing into consciousness the internal representational system which is her lead system, visual images internally generated.

Notice the generalization here is that in the case of a client who desires psychotherapeutic assistance and who has a mismatch between her representational system and her lead system, one particularly powerful choice is to re-align those two systems to that they coincide. Thus the hypnotist may work to bring the lead system to consciousness and thereby give the client choices by giving her conscious access to her lead system, or by making her representational system the lead system. Whichever choice the hypnotist makes, the result is that the client's lead and representational system coincide—a state of congruity.

We proceeded consistently with principles presented earlier; (1) induction into trance is enhanced to the degree that the client pays increasing attention to internally generated stimuli to the exclusion of externally based experience : the shift from the e superscript to the i superscript; and (2) induction into trance will involve pacing the client, meeting her at her model of the world : the client's R operator. Thus, the authors paced Lindsay effectively by responding with kinesthetic predicates and using the principle of representational system overlap, we led Lindsey into an altered state of consciousness: specifically, she became aware of visual images internally generated. This altered state served as a reference experience and gives her a choice through which she can access into consciousness (the altered state) the visual images which are the sources of the feelings of depression she experiences. Lindsey proved to be a rather alert and rapid learner and succeeded in achieving the altered state quickly. Had she experienced any difficulty in this process, the authors would have, as we have with other clients, paced her consciousness with kinesthetic predicates (her R operator is K) while simultaneously marking out portions of our ongoing communications with visual markers (her L operator is V); that is, specific body postures, hand and arm movements, facial expressions,...to covertly induce an altered state from which we could assist her in creating the altered states of consciousness she needed to have a choice about her "problem."

One additional comment can usefully be made regarding the Lindsey transcript. We have noticed a tendency among the hypnotists who we have had the opportunity to work with to rely on relatively ritualistic and mechanical induction procedures in developing altered states of consciousness with their clients. The result of such activity is the creation with their clients of a relatively homogenous altered state of consciousness which is the hypnotist's Complex Equivalence for trance. Typically, the hypnotist involved will then carry out the therapeutic, dental or medical work to be accomplished. In the cases where this procedure is successful, we applaud. However, these hypnotists often report to us that they encounter resistant clients and that the work which they perform in the altered state is not always successful. In those cases, we strongly recommend that to the hypnotists involved that they increase their own flexibility in their induction and utilization procedures and further that they tailor the altered state of consciousness that they create with their clients precisely to the needs of the clients. There are as many altered states as there is creativity on the part of each person who works as a communicator or explores his own consciousness. The mixture of the externally generated and internally generated states are infinite. We would recommend to the reader that he create for himself as many choices as possible — keeping in mind that the creation of an altered state or trance is useful for some purpose. Some altered states will be more useful for certain purposes than others. Part of the real art of hypnosis, and communication in general, is the ability of the communicator to assist those he communicates with to achieve a desirable state for the purposes of the communication. The 4-tuple model with the $\left\{ {i \atop e} \right\}, t/p\ A_d, R$ and L distinctions offered a very specific way of generating altered states.

We wish to offer a meta-comment at this point regarding generalizations such as the one regarding visual accessing clues. In our opinion, there is no substitute for the communicator/ hypnotist developing his or her ability to make finer and finer sensory distinctions — there is no substitute for the ability to see, hear, feel and smell. The underlying theme which runs consistently through our work — the purpose of the various models which we have created whether in *The Structure of Magic* series (with Virginia Satir), the *Patterns* series or the *Changing with Families* — is to develop models which tune people who use the models to their sensory experience. We offer these models as a way to create sensory experience for yourselves — essentially a set of sensory distinctions and patterns of those sensory distinctions.

In our experience, there is a strong tendency for theories or models (particularly statistic models) to replace or be used in substitution for experience. Statistical studies, for example, which state that a certain percentage of the general population is hypnotizable, or capable of some set of deep trance phenomena are frequently used by some practitioners of hypnosis as an explanation when they do not adequately pace and lead a client into an altered state of consciousness. We have two comments regarding such studies: first, we understand such studies to be simply a test of the effectiveness of a particular set of specified inductions or deep trance utilization techniques. As such, a set of rigid techniques constitute a model; and as with all models, such a set needs to be evaluated by how useful it is for the purposes it is designed. If the set of techniques yields the result that a high percentage of the population is hypnotizable or capable of deep trance phenomena, then the model is useful for those purposes; and we may begin to explore and develop ways to assist the small percentage of people who do not respond successfully to that rigid set of techniques to create those useful experiences. If the set of techniques yields results that claim a low percentage of the population is hypnotizable or capable of deep trance phenomena, then consistent with the scientific principles of model construction, such models should be junked. The only other justification for such models which we can conceive of is to convince practitioners of hypnosis that they should expect to fail with a certain number of their clients. As hypnotists, each of us is already aware of the power of such suggestions or self-fulfilling prophecies. Secondly, statistical studies rarely present in descriptive language distinctions in the sensory experience of either the hypnotist or the client, and thereby fail to provide the practitioners with a specific means to train him or herself to detect with sensory experience the response of the unique person who he or she is communicating with at that particular moment in time. The emphasis is typically on the techniques not on the response of the human being who is attempting to response to the technique. Erickson states the case quite adequately:

A primary problem in all hypnotic work is the induction of satisfactory trance states. Especially is this true in any work based upon deep hypnosis. Even the problem of inducing light trance states and maintaining them at a constant level is often a difficult task. The securing of comparable degrees of hypnosis in different subjects and similar trance states in the same subject at different times frequently constitutes a major problem.

The reasons for these difficulties derive from the fact that hypnosis depends upon inter- and intrapersonal relationships. Such relationships are inconstant and alter in accord with personality reactions to each hypnotic development. Additionally, each individual personality is unique and its patterns of spontaneous and responsive behavior necessarily vary in relation to time, situation, purposes served, and the personalities involved.

Statistically, certain averages may be obtained for hypnotic behavior but such averages do not represent the performance of any one subject. Hence, they cannot be used to appraise either individual performances or specific hypnotic phenomena. To judge trance depths and hypnotic responses, consideration must be given not only to average responses but to the various deviations from the average that may be manifested by the individual. For example, catalepsy is a fairly standard form of hypnotic behavior appearing usually in the light trance and persisting in the deep trance states. However, extensive experience will disclose that some subjects may never spontaneously develop catalepsy a single phenomenon either in the light or deep trance. Others may manifest it only in the lighter stages of hypnosis, some only in the profound trances, and some only in the transition from the light to the deeper levels of hypnosis. Even more confusing are those subjects who manifest it only in relation to other types of hypnotic behavior, such as amnesia. However good an indicator of trance states catalepsy may be on the average, its presence or absence for any one subject must be interpreted entirely in terms of that subject's total hypnotic behavior.

Efforts have been made to solve some of these difficulties by developing special techniques for the induction and regulation of hypnotic trances sometimes with little regard for the nature of hypnotic behavior. One of the most absurd of these endeavors, illustrative of a frequent tendency to disregard hypnosis as a phenomenon in favor of an induction technique as a rigidly controllable process apart from the subjects behavior, was the making of phonograph records. This was done on the assumption that identical suggestions would induce identical hypnotic responses in different subjects and at different times. There was a complete oversight of the individuality of subjects, their varying capacities to learn and to respond, and their differing attitudes, frames of reference, and purposes for engaging in hypnotic work. There was oversight of the importance of *interpersonal relationships* and of the fact that these are both contingent and dependent upon the *intrapsychic* or *intrapersonal relationships* of the subject.

Even in so established a field as pharmacology, a standardized dose of a drug is actually an approximation so far as the individual's physiological response is concerned. When thought is given to the difficulty of "standardizing" such intangibles as inter- and intrapersonal relationships, the futility of a rigid hypnotic technique to "secure controlled results" is apparent. An awareness of the variability of human behavior and the need to meet it should be the basis of all hypnotic techniques.

Another important general consideration in trance induction concerns the appreciation of time as a factor in itself. Traditionally, the mystic force of a simple glance from the eagle eye is sufficient to induce hypnosis. This misconception has not really been discredited since statements can be found in current literature to the effect that 2-5 minutes' time is sufficient to induce the profound neuro- and psychophysiological changes of hypnosis. When administering a powerful drug, these same writers would wait a reasonable time for its effects. The expectation of practically instantaneous results from the spoken word indicates an uncritical approach which militates against scientifically valid results. Unfortunately, much public work has been based upon an unrecognized belief in the immediate omnipotence of hypnotic suggestions and a failure to appreciate that responsive behavior in the hypnotic subject, as in the unhypnotized person, depends upon a time factor. The hypnotic subject is often expected, in a few moments, to reorient himself completely psychologically and physiologically, and to perform complex tasks ordinarily impossible in the nonhypnotic state.

Subjects vary in respect to time requirements, and their time requirements vary greatly from one type of behavior to another, and also in relation to their immediate frame of reference. Some subjects who can develop visual hallucinations promptly may require a relatively prolonged time to develop auditory hallucinations. The presence of a certain mood may facilitate or hinder hypnotic responses. Incidental considerations may interfere with the development of hypnotic phenomena ordinarily possible for the subject. The fact that the author is a psychiatrist has more than once militated against a subject's readily developing auditory hallucinations.

The oversight and actual neglect of time as an important factor in hypnosis and the disregard of the individual needs of subjects account for much contradiction in hypnotic studies. Published estimates of the hypnotizability of the general population range from 5-70 percent and even higher. The lower estimates are often due to a disregard of time as an important factor in the development of hypnotic behavior. Personal experience extending over 35 years with well over 3,500 hypnotic subjects has been the most convincing of the importance of subject individuality and time values. One of the author's most capable subjects required less than 30 seconds to develop his first profound trance, with subsequently equally rapid and consistently reliable hypnotic behavior. A second remarkably competent subject required 300 hours of systematic labor before a trance was even induced; thereafter, a 20-30 minute period of trance induction was requisite to secure valid hypnotic behavior.

Now, more specific discussion will be offered concerning the nature of deep trances and their induction, but not with any view of trying to describe a specific technical procedure. The variability of subjects, the individuality of their general and immediate needs, their differences in time and situation requirements, the uniqueness of their personalities and capabilities, together with the demands made by the projected work, render impossible any absolutely rigid procedure. At best, a rigid procedure can be employed to determine its effectiveness in securing certain results; as such, it is a measure of itself primarily and not of the inherent nature of the results obtained.

Milton H. Erickson, *Deep Trance and its Induction*, Haley (ed.), 1967, pp. 7-11.

Thus, when we state in the foregoing section that right handed people look up and to the left when they are accessing eidetic images, we wish to call your attention to the fact that you can come to understand a great deal about another person's experience by attending to their eye scanning patterns and that further, for a certain class of people (right-handed people) when they look up and to the left, they bring into consciousness visual images of actual experiences from the past. We offer this to you as a way for you to organize your experience make sensory distinctions which will enable you to be more effective in your hypnotic communication. Essentially, we present this to you as one particular way of seeing and utilizing non-verbal communications. As with every pattern in the models we have created, this is a generalization, and as with all generalizations, it will fail to be useful for some particular client at some particular point in time. We caution you then that when the generalizations or patterns we offer in our models do not match the sensory experience you have of the client you work with, the generalization is to be adjusted, not the human being. Further, you are to be complimented; your ability to detect the lack of match between the patterns we offer and the sensory experience you have of your client presupposes both that you have succeeded in internalizing the patterns presented in a model; a successful learning task accomplished by you, and more importantly, that you have tuned yourself in to the infinitely rich world of sensory experience.

Accessing Techniques

One of the principles which Milton H. Erickson, M.D. of Phoenix, Arizona, has emphasized over and again is that the client has in his or her history, experiences which, when properly utilized, can form the basis for the change they desire. If you accept this principle, then the question becomes how you as a hypnotist/communicator can access and utilize the client's experiences which will provide the resources for the changes desired. We proceed now to a presentation of specific techniques for accomplishing this.

Internal processing of information can occur in any representational system. Our understanding is that people make meaning out of language by accessing pieces of past 4-tuples. For example, most of you know what the word *comfort* means; but how many of you know how you know what the word *comfort* means? When the name, the word, is uttered, it serves as an anchor to retrieve the 4-tuple it is the name of. When I say *comfort* some past 4-tuple or set of 4-tuples associated with the name *comfort* is accessed internally. Some feeling, some picture, some sound and some smell are accessed at the unconscious level. Only a portion of this 4-tuple or set of 4-tuples will be accessed in consciousness. As the 4-tuple arises into consciousness or a portion of comes into consciousness, people typically use some body movement or eye scanning pattern to access the information. The information accessed is the meaning of the word or words. Let us return momentarily to one of the most fascinating aspects of communication — as you read the words on this page, they will convey meaning to you. Whether or not the exact meaning we intend is the one you will understand is very questionable, but you will have some "understanding" of what we are saying. The degree to which you understand what we intend will be the degree to which we have communicated. We have stated words can be understood as labels or anchors which trigger past 4-tuples. If we say or write the word *comfort,*how do you understand what its meaning is? Our understanding is that at some time you or someone around you was feeling comfort, and they labelled it, attached, if you will, an anchor to some experience. Perhaps this happened a number of times. And now when you hear the word it triggers or accesses at the unconscious level one or more of those past 4-tuples. At the unconscious level, a 4-tuple for comfort is accessed. You may be conscious of a portion of this, and feel, minimally, some comfort or see yourself or someone else being comfortable. This can be represented by the R operator on the 4-tuple accessed at the unconscious level. Meaning is made in present experience out of the sum total of past experiences. Frequently, in describing in words some previous experience, we so effectively access the entire set of 4-tuples at the unconscious level that the unconsciously accessed experience spills over into our present behavior and we re-live it; the couple, for example, who describe a previous quarrel so well that they end up fighting again. Erickson presents a personal example of the phenomenon:

While relating to a friend in great detail the events of a trip made ten years previously in the Rocky Mountains with a car having a floor shift the author, who was driving in a steering wheel shift car which he had driven for more than five years, suddenly saw a red light and sought frantically with his right hand to find the floor shift to put the engine into neutral while his friend watched in amazement. The car was stopped only by the expedient of jamming the brake and turning off the ignition before the author realized that the vividness and extensiveness of his memories about the past trip had extended over into the field of unrecognized associated motor memories.

> Milton H. Erickson, *The Confusion Technique in Hypnosis*, Haley (ed.), 1967, page 134.

Words are useful for communication in that they are anchors which trigger past 4-tuples. The word "horse" is meaningful if you have some experience of a horse, seeing it, touching it, hearing it, smelling it; either directly or through a movie or a picture of it. A human being who never had any contact with a horse or a representation of a horse would not have a meaning for the word. If you were communicating with this person verbally, you would perhaps describe it as big, with four legs, able to run very fast...The listener would access past experiences of big animals with four legs and experiences of fast animal in order to try to get an idea of the meaning that you as the speaker were trying to convey. Unicorns do not exist — yet we can understand the meaning of the word *unicorn* by combining an image of a horse with the tusk or horn of a narwhal. Constructed images of this nature can then serve as a reference structure for understanding just as primary experience does. What this means to the hypnotist/communicator is that any experience, whether internally or externally generated, can serve as a valid reference structure for future understanding and behavior. Further, past 4-tuples can be combined to make new 4-tuples which can serve as a future basis for understanding, learning and behavior. This is one of the most important patterns for the agent of change (psychotherapeutic) practitioner of hypnosis.

The notions of anchoring (both verbally and non-verbally) and Transderivational Search provide the hypnotist/communicator with precisely the tools needed to access and anchor or stabilize the resources from the client's own personal history which the client needs to make the changes he or she desires.

Let us digress a moment and review a portion of *Patterns I* on the subject of Transderivational Search. First keep in mind the important fact that all the verbal patterns have their counterparts in the analogue systems. For example, consider deletion — a linguistic phenomenon which has its counterpart in all representational systems. We delete a natural part of our unconscious modeling, much of what is available to us. One way to understand this is to consider the R-operator on the 4-tuple. Essentially, all the portions of our experience which is rare — not available in our consciousness. The notion of transderivational search also has its counterpart in the analogue system. First, let us review it briefly in the context of language patterns:

In our everyday communications with the people around us, we employ a set of language processing strategies which allow us to extract from the speech of others the meaning of the words, phrases and sentences which they use. These language processing strategies are the research domain for psycho-linguists (see, for example, references for Bever and for Slobin in the Bibiliography). Erickson has succeeded in utilizing these language processing mechanisms in a way which allows him to communicate with both the conscious and the unconscious portions of the client's mind. Essentially, he accomplishes this by presenting the client with a Surface Structure of English which activates the normally conscious mind-processing mechanisms. At the same time, he activates additional meaning recovery processes which develop meanings which are available to the unconscious portion of the client's mind but not of the conscious portion . . . We begin by reviewing the basic linguistic distinctions necessary for an understanding of these techniques (see *Magic I*, Appendix A, for fuller discussion).

Each sentence of every natural language has two distinct representations: the representation of the way it *actually sounds* (or, if written, the way it actually appears), called the **Surface Structure**, and the representation of the *meaning* which it has, called the **Deep Structure**. For example, when a person says the sentence:

The window was broken.

the Surface Structure is the representation of the actual sounds made by the person speaking, or, in the case of a written representation, the words written out, as above. In addition to this representation, this sentence is associated with another representation which is the meaning it has — the Deep Structure. In this particular case, the Deep Structure can be represented as:

PAST (BREAK [someone, window, with something])

This Deep Structure representation is designed to capture the intuition that each of us has as a native speaker of English that, when we hear the Surface Structure presented above, we understand the following:

(a) Some event occurred in the PAST;
(b) The event was a complex event having the following parts:

    (1) An action — BREAK — which occurred between:
        a. The agent — some person or thing doing the breaking — here represented by *someone;*
        b. The object — some person or thing being broken — here represented by *the window;*
        c. The instrument — the thing used to do the breaking — here represented by *with some thing.*

Notice that, even though not all of the parts of the Deep Structure representation appear in the Surface Structure (in this case, the agent and the instrument are not represented in the Surface Structure), the native speaker of English has that information available in his understanding of the sentence. The ways in which Surface Structures can differ from their associated Deep Structures in the research domain of tranformational linguists. They have postulated a series of formal mapping operations called transformations which specify precisely how Deep and Surface Structures may differ — the entire process which links a Deep Structure to its Surface Structure(s) is called a **derivation.**

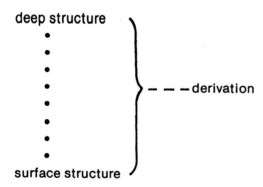

With these basic linguistic distinctions, we may begin a presentation of the patterns themselves.

Transderivatonal Search — Generalized Referential Index

One of Erickson's favorite devices, employed when the client is in both trance and "normal" state of awareness, is for him to tell a story. This story, typically, begins with the phrase: *I had a patient once...* Erickson then proceeds to describe some actual or created-on-the-spot version of an experience which will be relevant to the person to whom he is presently speaking. The amount of relevance which the story has depends upon how direct Erickson wishes to be in his communications; in general, this will depend upon the depth of the client's trance. Erickson employs the principle that the client will respond best if the relevance of the story is just outside the client's conscious awareness. This is an example of the transderivational search for meaning spurred by the use of a generalized referential index. If Erickson utters the sentence:

You can focus your eyes on the corner of...

the noun *you* has the referential index of the client — the person to whom Erickson is talking — and the client is conscious that Erickson intends the word *you* to refer to him. However, when Erickson says:

I had a patient once...

the client's normal linguistic processing mechanisms derive from that Surface Structure a Deep Structure meaning which contains no noun which refers to the client himself. Similarly, when a client hears the following phrases :

People *can make the most of* learning opportunities...
A man *once sat in that very chair and felt nervous*...
A waitress *wanted to have* an important thing *for self*...

he constructs for himself a Deep Structure which includes no occurrence of a noun which has his own referential index as a part. Erickson's behavior and the response which he secures from his clients, as well as our own experience and the responses which we consistently secure from our clients, have convinced us that there is an extra bit of linguistic processing which occurs at the unconscious level. The most useful model which we have found to assist us in organizing our own experience, as well as building a model for Erickson's work, is that of the transderivational search. This process operates as follows:

(a) The client hears a well-formed Surface Structure;
(b) The client recovers the associated Deep Structure and is aware of the meaning of that Deep Structure, one which has no direct reference to him;
(c) The client activates a transderivational search for at the unconscious level for an additional Deep Structure which is more relevant for his ongoing experience.

This last step requires more explanation. Clients do not randomly generate additional Deep Structures; rather, the Deep Structures which they generate are systematically related to the originally recovered Deep Structure. Specifically, they generate Deep Structures which are identical in form to the recovered Deep Structure except that they substitute nouns with referential indices which pick out portions of their ongoing behavior, thus making them maximally relevant for themselves. We illustrate by example. The client hears the Surface Structure:

People can make the most of learning opportunities.

The normal linguistic processing mechanisms apply, deriving the associated Deep Structure:

POSSIBLE (MAKE MOST [EVERY (people, learning opportunities)])

So, presenting the entire process to this point in a visual display, we have:

POSS (MAKE MOST [EVERY (people, learning opportunities)])

People can make the most ouf of learning opportunities.

Now, by the principle of transderivational search, the client begins the unconscious process of finding a Deep Structure which is identical in form to the recovered Deep Structure with nouns with referential indices relevant to his ongoing experience, substituted into the positions of the nouns which are in the recovered Deep Structure but which have no referential index relevant to the client's ongoing experience. Therefore, the newly generated Deep Structures will be identical to the recovered one with new nouns substituted in those positions. The client will generate, among others, the following Deep Structure:

POSSIBLE(MAKE MOST [I, this specific learning opportunity])

In other words, among the Deep Structures identical with the one originally recovered is the one above — one which has the associated Surface Structure:

I (the client) can make the most out of this learning opportunity

Thus, by the process of transderivational search, the client generates the meaning which is maximally relevant for his ongoing experience. By this technique, Erickson successfully paces the client's ongoing experience, allows the client maximal freedom to create meaning for himself and, thereby, participate actively in the process of communication, and avoids instructing the client in a way of which he is conscious (no "resistance" could possibly arise as no direction to resist has been given by Erickson)....

In other words, the client recovers the Deep Structure which corresponds to the Surface Structure Erickson utters, then he generates a series of Deep Structures identical up to the referential indices. From this set, the client then selects the Deep Structure which is most relevant for his ongoing experience.

> *Patterns of the Hypnotic Techniques of Milton H. Erickson, M.D.*, Volume I, p. 217-222.

We now extend this notion explicitly to the analogue systems and say that the listener in this situation not only generates a set of well formed deep structures, but also the corresponding sets of 4-tuples from which the deep structures themselves were derived. Thus, words are anchors for past 4-tuples—phrases are sequences of 4-tuples which combine into meaningful patterns of conscious and unconscious understanding.* When we ask a question, it is in essence a request for the person responding to bring into consciousness the result of a transderivational search. I might, for example, as you, when was the first time you met Milton H. Erickson, M.D.? If you are a person with a highly visual representational system, you might first picture Milton and then flip through a series of backgrounds till you saw the right one. If you are a person with a highly developed kinesthetic representational system, you might have a certain feeling which triggers the body sensations associated with a certain place and time which identify your experience of Erickson. If you are a person with a highly auditory representational system you might hear the sound of Milton's voice, and listen attentively to the surrounding noises to recover the time and place. All these example of transderivational search in analogue sytems. Words serve to access understandings working as anchors for past 4-tuples, combining them at the conscious as well as at the unconscious level to make "new meaning" or just triggering past memories (4-tuples) intact.

Words, however, are not the only anchors which trigger past 4-tuples. Any portion of any variable of any past 4-tuple can serve as a trigger to access the full past 4-tuple. Check your own experience—have you ever gone into an older person's home and the smell sent you back to memories of your grandmother's house? Or have you ever been walking down the street and smelled the scent of fresh-cut grass and went back to childhood memories of your father cutting grass. The O variable of the 4-tuple has, in our experience of selecting and using different lead system in the process of transderivational search proven itself consistently the most powerful choice for moving rapidly through time and space. Having a client smell their blankie, cookies in their grand mother's house. . .produces immediate and profound age regression. The olfactory tracts are the only one of the sensory tracts which do not pass through the thalamic area, having direct cortical projections.

Have you ever seen someone who reminded you of an old friend and thought about some experience you enjoyed with that friend? When a couple says: "they are playing our song," they are explicitly stating that a certain song is an anchor which accesses memories of 4-tuples of some other time and place and likely the pleasures that went along with the past 4-tuple of falling in love. Photographs in the family album, jingles for coca cola, sound effects in the movies, are all examples of anchors that are familiar to all of us in this culture. Transderivational search is such a common feature of our spontaneous, typically unconsciousness behavior that people in our Training Seminars have some initial difficulty in identifying it.

Perhaps some of you have had the following experience. You are ready to leave the house but you are unable to find your car keys. One sequence of transderivational searches you might go through would be the following: First you might ask in words (A^e_d as lead in the Transderivational Search) whether anyone knows where your car keys are (essentially, getting other people to do the Transderivational Search for you). Next you might attempt to visualize (V^i as lead) where you left them. You might then listen (A^i_t as lead) to the sound the car keys made hitting the surface you put them down on. Finally, you could walk over the the door (where you know for certain you last had them with you) and walk into the house (K as lead) again to re-activate the motor programs from the time/space coordinates in which you last had the keys. The strategy of using the different variables of the 4-tuple $(A_d A_t, V, K, O)$ as lead/representational system (L and R operators) in accessing and organizing experience presupposes that you have a choice of altering your consciousness. Our experience leads us to believe that when we understand language, the A_d portion of the complete Complex Equivalence (the word plus the 4-tuples which is the meaningful segment of language. Typically, we experience in consciousness only the portions of the 4-tuple(s) which are in our most highly valued representational system (the R-operator).

We first began to suspect that the whole past 4-tuple is accessed by naming it when as hypnotists we began asking clients and participants in our seminars and workshops whether they had ever been in a deep trance. Similarly at lectures we would frequently ask people if they had ever met Milton H. Erickson M.D. of Phoenix, Arizona. Preceding or concommitant with an affirmative answer to this question, the person with whom we were talking would drop into trance momentarily. If we lifted their left arm catalepsy was evident and a few suggestions would deepen the trance with ease. We also had learned from Milton H. Erickson that it is useful to give clients a signal for re-induction after a deep trance had been obtained to facilitate an immediate return to deep trance should it prove useful at some later date. This re-induction signal could be a word, a particular tonal quality to my voice, a kinesthetic sensation such as a squeeze on the wrist—in fact, any part of any variable of the 4-tuple of deep trance. At first, we thought of these as simple post-hypnotic suggestions? But what does it mean to carry out post-hypnotic suggestions? Thus, we now find it more useful to regard re-induction signals as a special type of anchor; an anchor which accesses the 4-tuple of deep trance. This explains what makes amnesia for post-hypnotic suggestions possible—they are 4-tuples and anchors for 4-tuples which are in∿R systems and therefore are disassociated enough that conscious access by the client's normal R operator is not available. The post-hypnotic behavior of trance subjects and ordinary people carrying out TOTES such as shaking hands, lighting a cigarette, turning the page, or answering the telephone is very similar. In both states, if the subject is interrupted, there is a momentary lack of response and, if useful, a trance can be easily induced almost instantly. In both cases eye dilation is evident, and in both cases raising of the client's arm reveals catalepsy. In fact, we have found that marking a word in a sentence, either tonally, visually, or kinesthetically, accesses whole 4-tuples associated with the experience named. For example, late one night in an evening seminar some of the students began to tire and become sleepy when the circumstances required full attention. One of the authors asked the group if they had noticed anyone exceptionally ALERT (this word was marked with exaggerated tonality) in the group tonight and they did.

Erickson has detailed an exquisite example of the use of kinesthetic transderivational search as a trance induction. Notice how in the following excerpt Erickson instructs the boy to use the K variable of the 4-tuple which he desires to access to transport himself back through time and space.

Another highly technical and complicated procedure of trance induction was developed that summer and repeated in many variations, but with no real understanding at that time of what was involved. A sixteen-year-old boy, who regularly drove a milk wagon, had never before been hypnotized. He was asked to sit quietly in a chair and silently review in his own mind every feeling throughout his body as he systematically recalled the events of the twenty-mile milk route over which he regularly drove a team of horses. The further explanation was given that, even as one can remember names, places, things and events, so could one remember body feelings of all sorts and kinds. This he was to do by sitting quietly in the chair with his eyes closed and to imagine himself driving along the highway, feeling the reins in his hands and the motions of the wagon and of the wagon seat.

Shortly it was noticed that he was shifting his hands and body in a manner suggestive of the actual experience of driving a team of horses. Suddenly he braced his feet, leaned backward, and presented the appearance of pulling hard on the reins. Immediately he was asked, "What are you doing now?" His reply was, as he opened his eyes, "Going down Coleman Hill." (The writer himself had often driven that same milk route in the same wagon and recognized the characteristic behavior of handling the team in going down that steep tortuous hill!)

Thereafter, with his eyes open and obviously in a somnambulistic trance, although he continued to sit in the chair, the boy went through a long, slow process of seemingly driving the horses, turning now right, now left, and heaving with his shoulders as if lifting cans of milk, thus reliving largely the experience of actually driving the milk route. The writer's own experience with that same milk route permitted a ready recognition of the progress being made along the route.

However, at one particular stretch of the road where there were no farm houses, the boy went through the motions of pulling on the reins and calling "whoa!" He was told to "drive on" and replied "Can't." After many futile efforts to induce him to continue driving and always eliciting the same response of "Can't," he was asked why he couldn't. The laconic reply of "Geese" was given. The writer immediately recalled that on infrequent occasions in his own experience a certain flock of geese happened to choose the moment of the milk wagon's arrival to cross the highway in single file on their way to another pond, thus stopping traffic.

This first trance lasted several hours as the boy went through the events of the "trip," and it seemed impossible to break into and interrupt it. Not until he turned the horses into the home driveway could the trance be terminated.

This particular trip was repeated in later similarly induced trances with similar results. The boy was also asked to relive other trips, in none of which the geese happened to appear, but his neglect of the established practice of letting the horses rest at a certain customary spot was disclosed in one such reliving.

At the same time of this work, there was no recognition by the writer of kinesthetic memories and iamges as a trance induction technique, but it led to a systematic and profitable investigation of the possibility of using any sensory modality as a basic process in inducing hypnotic trances.

Milton Erickson, *Historical Note on the Hand Levitation and Other Ideomotor Techniques*, Haley (ed.), 1967, pages 89-90.

We wish to emphasize Erickson's closing statement:

> ...systematic and profitable investigation of the possibility of using any sensory modality as a basic process in inducing hypnotic trances.

Indeed, the generalization of the notion of transderivational search from the verbal system (the A_d operator) to all the variables of the 4-tuple (A_t, K, V, O) is the representation in the model we are presenting of the "...systematic and profitable investigation of the possibility of using any sensory modality...".

Those of you reading this book who have had any direct experience of Gestalt work will recognize the same formal pattern as it occurs in the context of Gestalt therapy. Typically, the Gestalt therapist notices that the client is experiencing difficulty responding in the present time/space coordinate, and will instruct the client something like the following:

> Now I want you to stay with those feelings, ..., in fact intensify those feelings and let yourself drift back to some other occasion on which you had exactly those same feelings.

Essentially, the Gestalt therapist is instructing the client to use the K variable of their ongoing 4-tuple as the lead system for a transderivational search to access the set of past 4-tuples which have the same body sensations (K variable held constant) which constitute the "unfinished business" which is preventing the client from having the choice of remaining in the present and responding creatively. The so-called body therapies are an excellent example of the use of the K system as an accessing device.

The process of transderivation search is constantly at work. This accounts for the mixture of the externally and internally generated experience that constitutes the state that most of us live in. In fact, most of the work that the authors have done in the field of communication can be understood as providing specific techniques to allow the communicator to stay in up-time: that is, to have no consciousness of the transderivational search process while remaining congruent and creative in his responses. This allows him to have the maximum amount of sensory experience by using his 7 ∓ 2 chunks of attention focused on externally generated experience. Take, for example, the Meta Model for language we presented in volume I of *The Structure of Magic*. This set of language patterns is designed to allow communicators/therapists to communicate verbally with a client about his difficulty by asking questions based on form of the language he uses as opposed to the content. So when a client says "I'm scared" the listener detects the pattern of syntactic deletion: (see *Magic I*, Chapters 3 and 4) and responds by asking for the missing portion of the language representation — "Scared of what specifically?" This allows the communicator to respond appropriately without going into down-time (transderivational search within himself) to understand the communication at the content level. The communicator in the context of therapy who has learned the Meta Model has a TOTE which allows him to respond effectively and creatively to the client's utterance (of sentences with a deletion) without being forced to remember what it feels like to be scared. Thus when the client says "I'm scared", the communicator does not need to respond by accessing feelings and experiences of past fear. Having this choice allows him to be effective for the purposes of therapy. Specifically, it first keeps him from mixing up his experiences with that of the client, (traditionally referred to as projection and countertransference) and second, it allows him to stay in up-time to attend to sensory experience to detect all the important analogue messages that are constantly being offered by the client. Each moment of down-time is a moment of lost communication and the agent of change cannot afford to miss any messages if he is going to assist his client in accomplishing powerful and lasting change.

As we stated earlier, most of the learning that occurs is primarily the sequencing of already available unconscious TOTEs into new configurations, and with new content. As hypnotists/

therapists/communicators, it is a powerful learning to realize that clients who come for assistance of any kind already have all the resources they need to make the changes and accomplish their goals. The help they need from us as communicators is to organize the resources they already have in a way which is useful for their particular needs. In fact, as hypnotists, it is important to understand that each person has at some time in his life had an experience in which he displayed the very resources he needs to accomplish the changes he presently wants to make. Consider, for example, the so-called deep trance phenomena of positive and negative hallucinations. As children, we hallucinated freely in all systems as a learning technique: playing house, cowboys and Indians,.... Negative auditory hallucinations (not hearing what someone says) are a major part of most people's everyday life. The hypnotist need only organize these otherwise rather random abilities to be utilized in a directed fashion for the specific purposes of the hypnotic encounter. If we as communicators, for example, ask a client to access five times when they have been really creative in their past, and attach to the accessed 4-tuples the verbal anchor of "creative part," we then have assisted that client in organizing his past experiences and learnings in such a way as to create a 'creative part.' When we then later ask them to use this creative part, the verbal label, the anchor, will access the common portions of the past creative 4-tuples. This is one way, therapists typically reorganize past experiences to assist clients in coping in the present. An experience guided by the therapist in using the "creative part" will then serve as a future reference structure for making meaning just as the word "unicorn" does. Anchoring of parts by name is, of course, only one way to anchor and reorganize resources and is an excellent choice for working with the client's conscious mind. Anchoring can be done covertly as well, since the client will be aware only of a portion of his and the hypnotist's ongoing communication. The hypnotist may anchor 4-tuples covertly selecting anchors (analogue markings) in any of the clients~R-representational systems. As clients unconsciously access 4-tuples, they can be anchored visually, kinesthetically, and tonally as well. As a client describes past creative moments, a specific touch (for example, a squeeze on the knee) can also be used as a way of anchoring 4-tuples to create a resource for the client. The use of anchors, whether convert or overt, constitutes one of the primary tools of the agent of change working with clients.

Erickson, during the many years he has spent systematically exploring these possibilities, has used all of the systems (A_d, A_t, V, K, O). At present, confined as he is to a wheelchair, his options are somewhat reduced. Our experience of him leads us to believe that his primary and most frequent choices of anchoring resources with his clients are verbal (A_d, especially metaphor, the subject of volume III of the Patterns series), the tonal and tempo (A_t) qualities of his voices and body postures shifts. This last is particularly interesting. When the client Erickson is communicating with has his or her eyes open, the systematic movements of Erickson's body is detected at the unconscious level visually by the client. When the client has his or her eyes closed, the systematic movements of Erickson's body are detected auditorily by the client as Erickson's voice is spatially dislocated — a feature of communication subtle enough that it lies outside the conscious appreciation of nearly everyone: thus, it constitutes a very powerful anchoring choice.

In summary then, the tools of transderivational search and anchoring constitute a set of basic techniques for the accessing and stabilizing of precisely the resources that a client needs in order to accomplish the change which they come to you for assistance with. By generalizing the notion of transderivational search from the verbal system to all variables of the 4-tuple, you as a hypnotist have a full set of powerful, simple and elegant choices as to how to proceed to assist the client in accessing the resources he needs. The use of anchoring, whether overt or covert, provides you with a full set of techniques for stabilizing the resources accessed by the transderivational search techniques for stabilizing the resources accessed by the transderivational search techniques for use in creating the new choices the client desires. Transderivational search and anchoring are purely formal patterns extracted from the natural meaning making processes employed by all of us typically at the unconscious level of functioning. As such they have two very powerful properties: first, they are a maximum pace of our ongoing unconscious process — that is, they are the explicit representation of the processes which we use spontaneously. As with all pacing patterns (and especially those which pace unconscious processes), this ensures that they will be powerful and effective tools of communication. Secondly, transderivational search and anchoring are names for two formal or process patterns. Since they are formal, they each effectively represent a potentially infinite number of hypnotic communication choices — they can easily be adapted for any particular content situation. Finally, as the astute reader will have already noted, the pattern we call trans-derivational search is the name of the process of using some particular lead system (the L operator) to access and/or organize experience.

We introduce one final distinction into the 4-tuple model, that of congruency. Suppose, for example, that you as a hypnotist ask the client if he has ever been really creative and the client responds verbally "Yes" however shakes his head *no* at the same time, the communicator will have to do more than just anchor. He will have to communicate with more than just one part of the client simultaneously. This brings us to the next topic and the next distinction in the 4-tuple, the C operator. Very often your client will have more than one part which is communicating at a single point in time. All the communication will be a valid and useful representation of the client's experience. The effective com-municator will need a way to organize his experience in order to know how to communicate to the client who presents multi-messages, especially those which do not agree with each other.

The C-Operator

Once you understand the limitations of consciousness you can begin to understand both the necessity and usefulness of unconscious programming of behavior. At any point in time, t_1, a person has some experience, that is, a 4-tuple. His R operator determines what portion of that 4-tuple will be consciously represented to him. The rest of the 4-tuple occurs and is stored in memory and can be accessed into consciousness at some later time. However, it is not represented consciously at the time t_1, when that 4-tuple initially occurs. This process of selective awareness is both necessary and useful, but like any other useful process of human modeling, it can also be used in a way that immobilizes a person. R-operators on experience allow us as human beings to process information in amounts we can handle. However if we organize ourselves in such a way as to apply the R-operator that we delete important information such as signals of physical danger, this unconscious choice on consciousness can have a negative result. For our purposes here, it is sufficient to note at any time, t_1, there will both R and $\sim$R on a 4-tuple, such that the following would be possible.

$$R < V, \ K, \ A_t, \ O > \ ----> (V)$$
and
$$\sim R < V, \ K, \ A_t, \ O > \ ----> (K, \ A_t, \ O)$$

A few examples will help to clarify:

Joel says to his wife Martha in a harsh tone, "I really liked dinner, dear." She turns to him and says, "Well, if you think you can do better, do it yourself." She begins to leave the room; he says, "What's the matter with you? I said I liked it." His voice is angry but his facial expression is cowering and palms are turned up. He turns to one of the authors and shrugs his shoulders. This kind of communication is commonplace to the astute observer/ listener. When Joel spoke to his wife Martha, her experience can be represented as if she had applied an R operator on the 4-tuple of that experience that represented only A_t into consciousness.

$$R < A_t, \ V, \ K, \ O > \text{------} > (A_t^e)$$
$$\text{Martha}$$

The words Joel used, how he looked. . .were not accessed into consciousness.

$$\sim R < A_t, \ V, \ K, \ O > \text{------} > (V, \ K, \ O)$$
$$\text{Martha}$$

Joel similarly was aware only of the digital (words) aspect, and his feeling when he spoke.

$$R(A_d < A_t, \ V, \ K, \ O >) \text{------} > (K^i, \ A_d^e)$$
$$\text{Joe 1}$$

As the authors elicited this information from both parties, they agreed, "it was just a misunderstanding." Happily Martha asked Joel if he would like a cup of coffee. As Joel mumbled, "Sure," he shook his head back and forth *no*. The authors waited patiently to discover how this would turn out. After a few minutes Joel yelled out, "Where's the coffee?" (incidently at the same time displaying an artificial smile to the authors), Martha returned only to state that she thought he had said *no*. Joel then said he didn't want coffee anyway.

How is one to make sense out of such experiences? To the astute person such communications will be the rule not the exception. How do Martha and Joel fail to represent the multiple messages being communicated? This question is vital to the student of human behavior. As the R-operator indicates, Joel is limited to what he can represent in his own behavior. if his own behavior is inconsistent and he represents only one part of the inconsistency, he is said to be incongruent although he will not be aware of it. We now define another operator on the 4-tuple, C for congruency. When the messages carried by the variables of the 4-tuple and A_d are consistent with one another, we represent this as:

$$C(A_d < V, \ K, \ A_t, \ O >) \text{------} > \text{Yes}$$

When the messages carried are not consistent with one another, we have:

$$C(A_d \ < \ V, \ K, \ A_t, \ O \ >) \ \text{------>} \ No$$

The C operator determines whether or not for any specific 4-tuple(s) being experienced or expressed at a point in time, t_1, the values for the variables A_t, V, K, O, and A_d are consistent in meaning. For example, when Joel says (A_d) Yes and shakes his head "no" (K) the message value of the two of the variables are inconsistent:

$$C \ (A_d < V, \ K, \ A_t, \ O >) \ \text{------->} \ no$$

If a person were to communicate with words "yes" while shaking his head up and down, sounding and looking affirmative, such that all his output channels have messages which have meanings which match, then he would be said to be congruent:

$$C \ (A_d < A_t, \ K, \ V, \ O > \ ) \ \text{------>} Yes$$

Similarly when Martha represents this same communication by Joel of a verbal *yes* and a visual *no*, and she has conscious access only to the visual dimensions of her experience, (her R-operator is V), she will not be aware ($\sim$ R is K, O, A, A) of the *no* message. The disassociation of two simultaneously presented inconsistent messages allows Martha to respond to these two inconsistent meanings from the world. However the unconscious portions of the inconsistent 4-tuple (R variables) are still accessed present.

Let us take another example. In a family therapy session Frank tells Mary he loves her. As he does this he slowly and unconsciously (involuntarily) moves his head back and forth *no*. Mary looks at him knitting her eyebrows. The therapist asks Mary if she believes Frank. She again hesitantly replies *yes*. The therapist asks Mary about the hesitant tone of her *yes*. She replies, "I don't know—it's just a feeling. I can't get a handle on it." In this case when Mary was presented with incongruent communication the R-operator brought the verbal message A_d into consciousness, however the visual message which was in~R was represented kinesthetically. In the session described, the therapist accused Mary of not being totally honest. This accusation was a gross and ungraceful simplification of the complex processes at work in this communication. The therapist had failed to observe Frank's incongruent communication, let alone to try to understand its source. And it is that source we wish to now discuss. Was Frank lying or was it accident that his head moved? These two answers are both inadequate with respect to the complexities of human beings. Any incongruent communication by a person is a reflection of two (minimally) inconsistent models for their behavior. Since consciousness is a limited phenomenon and the R-operator determines what will be represented, then as the R-operator shifts (as it typically does for most people), then separate representations can be constructed and thus separate models which may or may not be consistent with respect to being guides for their behavior are created. Check your own experience, have you *seen* something you wanted to try, but *felt* it was too dangerous. Or conversely perhaps you have *felt* a longing for something in your life, but *saw* it as to risky to try for. These are common expressions and are frequently the result of inconsistent representations or models for the same experience. If such inconsistent models are expressed simultaneously, then the result is incongruency such as the examples described above. (See Part II, *The Structure of Magic*, volume II for further discussion.)

The usefulness of the C-operator distiction is most evident in the case of hypnotic communication with clients who are incongruent — that is, clients who have more than one model for their behavior and these model are inconsistent with one another. To review briefly, there are two logical possibilities when the client the hypnotist is working with has inconsistent models— either the client expresses the conflicting models simultaneously or the client expresses the conflicting models sequentially. The first case—that of simultaneous incongruity—can be represented, as we have stated:

$$C (A_d <V, K, A_t, O>) \quad \text{------>no}$$

In other words, the messages carried by at least two of the output systems do not match—this indicates to the hypnotist that the client has conflicting models and that effective hypnotic communications will require that he communicate multiple messages simultaneously to each of the models involved. The second possibility—that of sequential incongruity—can be represented as:

$$\bar{C}\ (\ C\ (A_d < \ V,\ K,\ A_t,\ O >)_{t_1}\ \wedge\ (\ C\ (A_d < \ V,\ K,\ A_t,\ O >)_{t_2} \text{-----} > \text{no}$$

while both

$$C\ (A_d < V,\ K,\ A_t,\ O >)_{t_1} \text{-------} > \text{yes}$$

and

$$C\ (A_d < V,\ K,\ A_t,\ O >)_{t_2} \text{-------} > \text{yes}$$

The symbol $\bar{C}$ is used to identify the consistency operator when it is used to compare the consistency of two or more complete 4-tuples at two or more distinct moments in time. Such is often the case with clients who come for hypnosis for weight control. They congruently state that they want to lose weight, but when they try to maintain a diet they inevitably fail. During the time t_1 when they are expressing the desire to lose weight they are congruent— that is, there is no model which contradicts the desire to lose weight. However there is a model or models whch contradicts the desire to not eat. Such models are often stronger than post hypnotic suggestions, and in fact, work in much the same way. A series of TOTES which constitute the act of going to the kitchen and eating, are both disassociated and programmed to respond to an anchor represented in one of the variables of the 4-tuple. So very often the well meaning client is only discouraged to find him or herself half-finished with a consciously unwanted trespass on their vow of not eating. Many clients trigger the TOTE sequence by internal imagery of food, or the mention of food with internal dialgoue, this anchor is typically not represented in consciousness (that is, it is ~R). Thus the sequence is fired and the sin committed. Client will often get hungry at the mere mention of food, just as the average person will automatically extend his hand for a hand-shake at the slightest indication it is appropriate. Such sets of behaviors are almost involuntary unless the deliberate awareness is used to control them. The limits of conscious representation, however, prevent long term concentration and so the smoker will smoke, the obese will eat, until reprogramming creates some pervasive change in the intact series of TOTES. Further, if the trigger or anchor which initiates the series of TOTES is in~R for the client, they will not have the choice of bringing it into consciousness as a way for regaining choice and control over their own behavior.

In terms presented previously, these particular forms of incongruency are examples of the split between lead system and representational system where the contents of the two systems are inconsistent* Part of the job of an effective communicator hypnotist will be to access all parts or models of the client they are working with particularly relevant to the changes the client wants. For example, in the case of sequential incongruity, it will be particularly important for the communicator/hypnotist to access the parts of the client, the models which in the past have sabotaged all attempts at weight loss or any other type of habit control such as smoking, nail-biting...By accessing models which would otherwise express themselves sequentially after the session, sequential incongruity is converted into simultaneously expressed incongruity, thus allowing the communicator to communicate with all models at the same time.* In this way all the parts of the client are available as resources to produce the desired change instead of just a portion which will be overpowered by other parts at some later time. Here the hypnotist/communicator will do well to insure he or she has a full range of choice in their own verbal and non-verbal repertoire of communication skills. With regard to this, we mention in passing the techniques of asking the client to pretend they are different and noticing incongruities, asking the client to speculate freely about how their life would be different if they had accomplished the change (essentially the Meta-Model question for modal operators — "What would happen if you did?"), playing polarity (see Part II, *The Structure of Magic*, volume II), asking the client to pretend to *not* want to make the change and then demand that he explain why they don't want to....

The usefulness of a communicator/hypnotist understanding and being able to detect and utilize incongruency, is of vital importance. In our training seminars many hypnotists ask for techniques for working with resistant clients. Our understanding of resistance is that some part of a person is not willing to cooperate with the hypnotist, say, for example, in the context of a trance induction, even when the client verbally has stated a desire to go into a trance. If the hypnotist/communicator does not use up-time strategy and does not detect the multiple messages of an incongruent client, then he will meet resistance. If he detects multiple messages and does not have the tools to pace, and communicate with more than one model of a single client at the same time, then he will meet resistance. If he detects multiple messages and does not have the tools to pace, and communicate with more than one model of a single client at the same time, then he will also typically meet resistance. Resistance, in our understanding, is a lack on the part of a communicator to detect, communicate with and utilize creatively all parts of a client.*

We break the following discussion into two parts, first communication with congruent clients (where $C(Ad < At, V, K, O>)$ = yes) then secondly the incongruent client case (where $C(Ad < At, V, K, O>)$ = no).

Patterns of Meaningful Communication in Hypnosis with Congruent Clients

Communication in hypnosis or in any context for that matter is meaningful to the degree that it serves the desired purpose. To chat over morning coffee is meaningful to serve the purpose of amusing a friend, or the sharing of thoughts. Simple conversations during the day of an average person may sometimes serve his purposes, and sometimes he may be understood. Sometimes he is aware is he is misinterpreted when he is not. Sometimes he believes he is misinterpreted when he is not. Sometimes he is misinterpreted in a way that assists another person greatly. The range of possibilities is immense and as the serious student of communication becomes more and more aware of the complexities and multi-messages involved in communication, he cannot help but be fascinated by the amount of really meaningful communication that goes unnoticed by all agents in the communication process. It is as if two simple conscious minds discuss matters of little importance while their unconscious minds communicate about matters of more importance. How does the inquiring mind come to see and hear such multi-messages in communication, and how does the hypnotist use them to assist his clients in going into a trance and make changes that are beneficial to him as a human being? Erickson has devoted his life to the exploration of these phenomenon, and if half of what he has incorporated into unconscious patterns of his own behavior can be formalized it will make a solid foundation for a science of communication.

The case of communicating with the congruent client in hypnosis is the simple one. Typically, when asked if they want to go into a deep trance, the answer is an emphatic-*yes*, voice tone-sure, body gesture responsively agreeing.* Almost any technique of induction will work to some degree; such congruent clients usually are capable of almost any hypnotic phenomenon, and also rarely need hypnosis for psychological assistance. They are most often encountered by the dental and medical practitioner or the experimental practitioner. People in pain or faced with the prospect of pain are usually very congruent about their desire to avoid it. They are the willing and effective subjects in demonstrations and classrooms. However this is not signal for the practitioner to become careless in his work. Quite the contrary, the congruent client offers the opportunity for the profoundly creative use of hypnosis. The patterns presented in Volume I of *Patterns* provides the hypnotist with a structure for verbal suggestions in trance induction and trance utilization. The sytematic use of these patterns in conjunction with one another and the non-verbal components of communication (the 4-tuple) offer the astute hypnotist a multitude of choices. But on what basis is he or she to make that choice? What in essence are the well-formed meta-patterns for induction of a congruent client?

Each client brings to the hypnotist a plethora of ideosyncratic ideas, beliefs, and past experiences which constitute his model or models of the world. However the processes by which that model of the world is constructed are not nearly so numerous or overwhelming. First, we need an organizing principle such as the 4-tuple, and an understanding that each client organizes his experience by applying an L-operator and an R-operator over the 4-tuples of his experiences. Each client will have highly valued representational system principle. If the clients' kinesthetic who watches the accessing cues and listens to the predicates for accessing and bringing information into consciousness by his clients. Hypnotists need to realize the importance of determining a client's R-operator, for example, induction of trance will in essence be shifts in the R-operator over the client's experience. To say that someone has shifted awareness from one representational system to another is to say that they have altered their consciousness. Visualizations where imagery of escalators and such are used will induce light trance in the client but will not alone enable him to achieve deep trance. Here the hypnotist has two general classes of choices. First, he may choose to use the overlap/intersection of representational system principle. If the clients kinesthetic representational system is accessed, the visual client will have altered his awareness more radically and he may then proceed into even deeper trance states. The Huxley article presented in volume I should be consulted as an example of this principle at work — the use of representational sytem shifts with a congruent client.

The second class of choices makes use of the fact that even when using V^i with a client who has V for an R-operator, the entire 4-tuple is accessed. The perceptive hypnotist can detect that visualization of an elevator, for example, serves not only to access the 4-tuple connected with seeing an elevator—but also accesses the feelings connected—the sound and perhaps the smell will also be accessed. Understanding and training himself to detect such changes in the client's non-verbal response and developing choices about utilizing the R response will provide the hypnotist with powerful choices. But such a simple and overt use of the accessing of past 4-tuples to construct meaningful sequences of experience for the induction of trance, powerful as it is, is only one way to use their tool. Once you understand and use the 4-tuple with its associated distinctions (e.g. R, C, L operators...) gracefully, you will begin to realize the vast number of choices it makes available. As a client's past 4-tuples are accessed, the whole experience, the entire 4-tuple, as well as the words used to describe it, are accessed: resources to be utilized to assist the client in change. What a vast array of potential for the student of hypnosis to explore!

Examples of the escalator-type of accessing are easily produced in your own experience. More sophisticated analogue marking is done by determining the client's most highly valued representational sytem and if the client is congruent, marking in the highly valued representational system or all systems simultaneously. So, for example, if a client who has a well developed and highly valued kinesthetic representational system comes for hypnosis, the hypnotist may gracefully and gently as a matter of course place one of his hands on the client's knee and the other on the client's wrist. Once this has been naturally and comfortably accomplished a set of meaningful messages can be marked out while talking to the client. (Capital letters indicate squeezing when speaking that word.)

Hypnotist: Ms P. You have expressed some fear about your ability to GO INTO A TRANCE and I would like to reassure you COMFORTABLY and with PLEASURE so that you can allow yourself the SATISFACTION OF LEARNING to BEGIN A

TRANCE, NOW I want to FEEL RELAXED, I and you are not CLOSED to this NOW (her eyes close). Trance will offer (her eyes open) a change to RELAX and LEARN, REALLY LEARN to BLINK (she blinks) and away your problems with...

Analogue marking of multiple messages in this way allows communication to take place with more than one part of the client. At the same time while a meaningful conversaton about the benefits to be obtained from trance are being described, another set of meaningful messages is being marked by squeezes which indicate a sequenced set of 4-tuples to induce trance.

Going into a trance
comfortably
pleasure
feel relaxed
I closed (phonetic ambuiguity for *eye* closed)
Relax
learn, really learn
blink

The 4-tuples associated with each marked word or phrase in this sequence are themselves a well formed sequence for the development of trance. Thus the repetitious verbage and often quoted ritualistic verbal inductions and repeating of hypnotic commands is nothing more than a trivial example of the trance inductions used by Milton H. Erickson in a sophisticated way. Instead of repeating a single word louder and over and over, the hypnotist using the 4-tuple model can utilize all the available channels of communication in a way that the 4-tuples themselves would be sequenced for the induction and utilization of hypnotic trance. Further using analogue marking allows accessing not only of one set of 4-tuples but double and triple sets simultaneously reinforcing the sequence of 4-tuples which lead into trance.

The astute reader will have noticed by this time that analogue marking as described here and in volume I, is just a special case of anchoring. Tonal or kinesthetic marking of verbal anchors is just one of many ways to create multi-message communication. Communicators can anchor the ongoing behavior of their client in a systematic way and get just as complex a result. For example if each time a client describes experience which approximates the desired altered state, the hypnotist may simply anchor this by a specific touch on the right shoulder. Then later a touch on that shoulder will elicit at the unconscious level the commonality of the anchored 4-tuples. Erickson presents an excellent example of this technique of overlap or intersection of 4-tuples (using in this particular example a verbal transderivational lead to access the appropriate 5-tuples).

Perhaps a very simple and easily understood example can be given to clarify this type of accumulation of minimal cues leading to a specific response: The rest of the family was out for the evening, I was ill but comfortably seated in a chair, Bert, aged 17, had volunteered to remain at home to keep me company although there was no such need. A casual conversation was initiated by Bert in which he mentioned the rush and turmoil of getting everybody dressed and fed and everything packed up for a past vacation trip to northern Michigan. (We were living in Michigan at the time.) Next he mentioned the fishing, the catching of frogs and a frog-leg dinner, the beach dinner and the sand that the smaller children managed to sprinkle over every item of food, and then the albino frog at the abandoned quarry we had found.

Next he described in vivid detail the turmoil of getting everything out of the summer cabin, the oversights, the hunting for misplaced items, the wandering off of the smaller children and the hurried search for them, the locking-up of the cabin, and the hungry tired state we were in when we arrived at Wayne County General Hospital near Detroit where we lived.

At this point, a vague notion passed through my mind to suggest to Bert that he might take car and visit some friends, but this idea vanished as Bert laughingly told of how his brother Lance particularly liked eating Grandma Erickson's fried chicken on the way back to Michigan from Wisconsin. With much laughter, he recalled another occasion in which his small brother Allan had amused everybody, and especially Grandma and Grandpa Erickson with his "bulldozer" pattern of eating, that is, holding his plate up to his mouth and systematically using his other hand to shove the contents of the plate slowly and steadily into his mouth.

Again, this time a clearer idea came to mind of suggesting that Bert take the car keys and go for a ride so that I could enjoy reading, but I forgot it as I recalled my father's amused comment on the absolute efficiency and speed of Allan's method of eating.

While we were laughing about this, Bert mentioned the trip to my brother's farm, and six-year-old Betty Alice's long solemn explanation to three-year-old Allan's worried inquiry about how the mama chickens nursed their babies, that chickens were not mammals and only mammals nursed their young. While we were laughing about this, a third time the thought came to mind of offering the car for the evening, this time most clearly, and I recognized why. In every item of reminiscenses, Bert was speaking of pleasant and happy memories based each upon the driving of a car. Yet not once had he actually said the word "car," the nearest he came to that was to say "packing up," "trip," "went to see," "way out to the old quarry," "down to the beach," "on the way back to Michigan from Wisconsin," and the trip to my brother's farm, and not once did he mention the word key — locking-up the cabin was as close as he came to that.

I recognized the situation at once and remarked, "The answer is 'No'." He laughed and said, "Well, Dad, you'll have to admit it was a good try." "Not good enough, I caught on too fast. You overemphasized trips in the car. You should have mentioned the picketing of Ned's place, where our car was serviced, Ed Carpenter from whom I bought the car, the ice-fishing trip which was in Emil's car but did involve an automobile. In brief, you restricted yourself to constant indirect mention of pleasure trips, always in relationship to us, it was always in our car. The inference to be drawn became too obvious. Do you really want the car?" His answer was, "No, I just thought I'd get a little fun out of getting you to offer me the car keys."

> Milton H. Erickson, The "Surprise" and "My Friend John," *Techniques of Hypnosis*, Haley (ed.), page 117.

One way we have found useful to organize our trance induction experiences is the notion of tracking. Tracking is the methodical organization of accessing 4-tuples in the client in such a way as to track him from one specific 4-tuple (present state $-S_1$) to another 4-tuple—S^i (deep trance, for example) with the minimum steps or 4-tuple accessed on the way. For instance, we frequently teach participants in our training seminars to use a technique called *the shuffle* to induce trance. A client is asked what experience they would have just before entering a deep trance. They are questioned methodically about what their experience would be, covering the values of all the variables in the 4-tuple. When they express a complete description, thereby accessing those 4-tuples, this experience is named *the before 4-tuple*. Clients typically find this terminology somewhat humorous. Usually, in addition to this verbal anchor, some trigger, such as a squeeze on the knee, is also used either overtly with a congruent client or covertly with an incongruent client) to ensure that the client can re-access the before 4-tuple when it is named later and the knee squeeze anchor is repeated.

Next, a complete description of the 4-tuple that would be the client's experience just after deep trance is taken, allowing the client to fully access all the portions of that 4-tuple both a verbal and K anchors are established. Then the client is told to make the before 4-tuple (K trigger fired simultaneously), the after 4-tuple (K trigger fired simultaneously) and then, the after 4-tuple (K trigger), the before 4-tuple (K trigger) and then both K triggers for both the before and the after 4-tuple simultaneously. Usually a deep trance results, as the client accesses the deep trance 4-tuple while passing from the before 4-tuple to after 4-tuple level.

Another technique which we sometimes use in lecture situations for demonstration purposes is to ask some member of the audience to compare the last thing they were aware of before they woke up this morning with a deep trance. If this question is congruently asked of someone who has been in a trance and the authors wait expectantly, typically a trance readily develops as the task of comparing the two named altered states requires that they be accessed, (that is, the 4-tuples for both experiences). Utilization of the ensuing trance provides a rapid means of inducing a profound trance. Tracking procedures of this kind can be accomplished most easily by simply asking a question which presupposes the 4-tuple desired be accessed. In a lecture situation during a discussion of this very topic, one of the authors turned to the audience and asked sincerely, "Do any of you know how it feels to have asthma?" An array of choking, gagging and coughing, followed by laughter, resulted. The important thing here is that people do what they talk about as they talk about it — accessing 4-tuples and then commenting on them. Questions are answered by then commenting on them. Questions are answered by accessing the relevant 4-tuples and using them as the basis of understanding and responding whether or not the person responding brings those accessed 4-tuples into consciousness. As someone describes happy memories, they feel, look and sound happy; as someone describes a terrifying experience they feel, look and sound terrified; as someone talks about an exceptionally good meal, they taste it; and the astute observer will be able to detect the movements of their mouth and tongue. The systematic accessing of 4-tuples by tracking or sequencing, whether overt or covert, with or without anchors, offers a structure for communication of multiple messages in ways that give meaning to the principle of maximal direction (see *Patterns*, volume I, pages 249-251).

In our work, we have developed communication, and of organizing our experience in the hypnotic encounter—experiences which we believe are common to many practicioneers of hypnosis. We present a discussion of three specific tracking models we have found useful in our experience of hypnosis. We urge you to experiment with these models, thereby increasing your effectiveness and grace in your work in hypnosis.

Tracking Model I

The simplest tracking model logically is one where the hypnotist tracks the client from the client's present state (S_1) to the desired state (S^i) directly in a single step. Let us use a trance induction as an example.

Once a gentlemen came to us for assistance; he wanted us to use hypnosis to help him find the solution to a problem. A brief interview disclosed that he was a surgeon by profession. From his own description of his work we deduced that when doing surgery, this gentleman entered an altered state where the focus of his conscious attention was on one and only one thing—the operation—and nothing could distract him. If the sounds or movements around him were to distract him it might prove to be fatal to his clients. We therefore asked him to review in detail the last interesting, successful operation he had performed—to review it with the same interest and diligence he has used when he was actually performing the operation. He was to go through each and every step of the operation, making sure nothing was overlooked and that he was to accomplish this with the same quality work this time that he always does. We explained that while his conscious mind was occupied with the operation we would speak privately with his unconscious mind. Within seconds a trance insued—we simply deepened it and began our work. The point of this is that the communicator with some creativity will succeed in finding a 4-tuple for almost any desired altered state in his client's own personal experience. This 4-tuple, once accessed, can be utilized as a resource to assist each client with his individual needs. We recommend that each of you identify common 4-tuples for states of consciousness which you find yourself repeatedly creating with your clients— for example, for general deep trance, 4-tuples such as day dreaming, highway hypnosis, the so-called hypnogogic state, boring lectures, sermons . . .

Tracking Model II for Sequencing of 4-Tuples

For either the induction of trance or the utilization of trance for some purpose, the model for sequencing of 4-tuples provides a viable option about how to proceed. Taking a client from any state S_1 to any other state of consciousness S^i can be accomplished by describing 4-tuples, preferably ones that the client has had such that the values of the variables of the 4-tuple of S_1 change fluidly to the values of the variables of the S^i. For example, the client is a willing and congruent person who wishes to learn about going into a deep trance. Questioning him regarding this and discussing his understandings with him gives the hypnotist the opportunity to watch accessing cues and listen to predicates. The present state of the client is one which might be called the waking state. In the process of questioning the client about his understanding, he will search transderivationally (L operator) to understand and respond. Thus portions of the client's present state 4-tuples are internal. The client has a mixed focus of attention between internally generated experience and externally generated experience. Suppose while trying to watch and listen to the hypnotist the client is visualizing and having internal dialogue; and further, that his R-operator on the 4-tuple is kinesthetic—that is, the client is aware only of his body feelings, such as feeling confused and overwhelmed.* The hypnotist quickly reviews the communication he has had with the client and began as follows: (Underlined words and phrases were analogically marked with tonal shifts and the dots . . . indicate pauses.)

Hypnotist: Do you *remember* reading a book in the outer office while waiting for your appointment?

Client: Yes.

Hypnotist: I noticed that you were reading that book and I like to try a little experiment with you *before we begin.* Is that alright?

Client: Sure.

Hypnotist: Now I would like you to *close your eyes,* and *see* that book open to the first page you read...and even though the words are not *clear* as they could be you just *keep looking* at that book *comfortably...watch it* closely and as you begin to breath *deeper* words can become *clearer* and clearer till you can begin to read that book just as you did before. It might assist you if noticed the *smell* of the paper and pretended you were feeling the binding as you hold that book and begin to read, now when I walked through the outer office you didn't even notice me you were so engrossed in that book...and it is easy to *become engrossed* in a book so *deeply* that you don't even hear the sound of those people around you who are talking..you might even become so engrossed in reading that book that you forget where you are and whom you're with... in fact this book may become another one you get engrossed in *even deeper...* so *deeply* engrossed that you lost track of time and your whole world became the world of the book in your...and your conscious mind may continue to read and enjoy that book while your *other mind listens* to me because you don't have to listen to me...in fact that will make it easier to become totally engrossed in that book your other can *lift up* one of your *hands* to your *face* so that I will know when your conscious mind is gone *off* reading and your other mind and I are along to get to work on the problem you want to solve...now the only important thing is that your conscious mind stay *off* reading that book and remember just what the most interesting *point* to your ear was. (The hand begins to lift up off his knee slightly, but appears to be having some difficulty.) You can turn the page when you

> need to...you can scratch your *face* when it
> itches...you've done that before without knowing
> about when you were lost in reading...(client's hand
> lifts off knee).

The sequencing of 4-tuples for the trance induction is simple—it requires only that the hypnotist be willing to explore the client's experience thoroughly enough to find experiences 4-tuples which would naturally lead from the client's present state, S_1, to the desired altered state which had occurred earlier in the hypnotist's waiting room (becoming engrossed in reading a book) as a way of tracking the client from attending to externally generated experience to attending exclusively to internally generated experience (shifting to 4-tuple superscripts from e to i). The hypnotist also effectively used a portion of the K variable of the internally generated 4-tuple of reading a book (turning the page) to track the client quite naturally to the 4-tuple of hand and arm levitation. This is a simple yet powerful example of the principle of 4-tuple overlap which allows the hypnotist to track the client into an altered state. Specifically, the overlap between the 4-tuple of reading a book, more specifically, turning the page and the 4-tuple of hand and arm levitation occurs in the K system. In both 4-tuples there is a completely automatic, comfortable unconscious movement (TOTE) of the hand and arm up. These common TOTEs provide a natural bridge to track from one state (S_1 = reading a book) to another state (S_i = hand and arm levitation), closer to the desired state (deep trance, S^n).

Just as words are anchors for past 4-tuples, so too is any portion of a variable of a past 4-tuple an anchor for the whole 4-tuple (experience). Of course, past 4-tuples can be arranged to track anyone to any experience we wish to create. In the preceding example it was easy for this client to start by remembering reading, then move to the 4-tuple of reading and then experience of becoming so engrossed in the reading that his external world began to disappear visually as well as auditory. From that point, it was a relatively simple to task to disassociate him for the purposes of trance utilization. Model II for the sequencing of 4-tuples requires that the hypnotist be able to discern what kind of an altered state will be required for the specific hypnotic purposes, whether psychotherapeutic, dental, or medical, and to be able to find the bridging 4-tuples in the client's past. This tracking model can be represented visually as:

$$S_1, S_2, \ldots, S_i \ldots, S_{n-1}, S_n$$

where

S_1 = present 4-tuple state of client S_n = desired 4-tuple state

and

S_2 thru S_{n-1} are a logical progression of 4-tuples from the client's personal history by systematically altering the variables such that they overlap.

This tracking model is especially effective with children as so much of children's experiences are altered states which approximate trance. For example, we often will ask a child client who is brought to us by his parents for hypnotic work if he knows about his dreaming arm. The hypnotist's analogue communication is a very important aspect of this maneuver. The hypnotist must look and sound genuinely excited and sincerely interested. Children are very sensitive communicators and detect incongruent communication quickly.

We then typically proceed as follows:

Transcript

Hypnotist: Do you know about your dreaming arm (hypnotist's voice tone, tempo and facial and other body message youthful, excited and somewhat conspiratorial)?

Child: No (looks intrigued and a bit confused)

Hypnotist: You mean nobody ever taught you about your dreaming arm?

Child: No.

Hypnotist: Would you like to learn?

Child: Sure.

Hypnotist: Do you promise not to tell anybody else?

Child: Yes (hypnotist eyes child with suspicion)...I promise I won't tell.

Hypnotist: Well, OK, I guess you can be trusted. What's your favorite TV program?

Child: Steve Austin.

Hypnotist: You mean the six-million-dollar man?
Child: Ya.
Hypnotist: Now can you *see the first scene* of your favorite epi-
           sode (analogical tonal shift)
Child: Ya.
Hypnotist: Now *close* your eyes...(hypnotist lifts up the child's
           left arm)...Now you keep watching Steve Austin and
           allow your arm to go down only as fast as you *watch*
           the whole show and the only thing you have to do is
           to remember just what your favorite part was and tell
           when you're done...take all the time you need to
           really enjoy it.

Typically this will be all the tracking that is necessary for the trance induction. The arm will go down slowly and cataleptically. As the child accesses eidetic images, the side of the body contralateral to the hemisphere with eidetic images can be gently manipulated and typically the client will have no awareness of the kinesthetic sensations as cerebral competition is occurring. We caution you to investigate with each child which hemisphere has the eidetic images. In many left-handers, the dreaming arm will be their right hand as the localization of functions (such as eidetic images) and in fact all cerebral functions will be hemispherically reversed. This can easily be checked by accessing cues—that is, by asking the child to make a picture of the house he lives in. If his eyes move up and to the right, then he is a reversed case and the cerebral competition between eidetic images and the K system will occur maximally when the right hand is lifted. If the child's eyes move up and left, like most right handers, then his dreaming arm will be the left arm. If appropriate, the child's arm can be gently stopped (thereby stopping the eidetic images) and a "psychological commercial" inserted such as: "How surprised will you be when you discover your dry bed is so comfortable?" Once the "commercial" has been inserted, the arm is released and the sequence of eidetic images runs off. Typically the child will have no conscious representation for the commercial. This also works well as an inducation for many congruent adult clients. We typically proceed by having them visualize the first scene from their favorite movie and then lifting their arm up and stating congruently to them to let their arm go down only as fast as their eyes close and they drop into a very relaxed state watching that movies from beginning to end. We have as a demonstration from time to time asked one of the members of the audience within reach a question about something which requires visualization—such as describing in detail the house they lived in as a youngster while commenting on it. While congruently asking for more and more details about the visual dimensions of the house, one of the authors will reach over lifting the left arm (if the person is a right hander) of the person with whom we are speaking. As the member of the audience continues their verbal description of the visual image they are making the left arm stays suspended cataleptically in the air until the description ends and their eyes refocus. We have the choice of utilizing the catalepsy as the beginning of a trance induction if the situation makes this maneuver appropriate. This model for the sequencing of 4-tuples offers a viable way of inducing trance either directly or indirectly. Describing experiences which themselves serve as anchors for internal experiences approximating more and more closely the altered states required. There is no limit to the possible ways of utilizing this type of a model to guide your behavior as a hypnotist if you are willing to use your own creativity and the experiential resources of your clients.

Tracking Model III — Constructing 4-Tuples

Tracking Model III—Constructing 4-Tuples

A third choice about how to organize your experience while doing hypnosis is the tracking model for the construction of 4-tuples. Again consistent with the Ericksonian principle that the client has the resources somewhere in his personal history to make the changes he has come to the hypnotist for assistance with, the hypnotist may choose to use the principles of transderivational search to find there past 4-tuples which already contain the elements of behavior required for the new choice or experience the client wants. This third model differs from tracking models I and II in that the specific 4-tuple that the client desires which represents the new choice or experience he has come to the hypnotist for assistance in getting does not exist in his past experience. Thus the hypnotist must access a series of different past 4-tuples from the client's personal history, each of which includes an element of the 4-tuple the client and the hypnotist are working to create. Suppose, for example, the client is a young woman who has great difficulty being assertive with older men. The hypnotist might select tracking model III and begin to question the client closely regarding the nominalization *assertive:* in other words, which specific set of feelings, voice tone, tempo and melodic qualities,, way of presenting herself visually constitutes being assertive with older men. As the hypnotist discusses this with the client, the client will be demonstrating based on her past experience her understanding of being assertive. As a natural part of this communication interchange the hypnotist may ask the client if she has ever felt that particular way, or sounded that particular way...Typically, the client will reply that she has indeed but never with older men, or not since she was a young girl or. .In other words she will offer a series of disclaimers which disqualify any single one of her past experiences as an appropriate model 4-tuple for her being assertive with old men in the present. In the course of this interchange, the hypnotist establishes a series of anchors (either overt or covert) for the individual portions of the other words she will offer a series of disclaimers which disqualify any single one of her past experiencs as an appropriate model 4-tuple for her being assertive with old men in the present. In the course of this interchange, the hypnotist establishes a series of anchors (either overt or covert) for the individual portions of the series of 4-tuples, each containing a portion of the desired 4-tuple. Once the component parts of the desired 4-tuple are anchored, having been extracted from a series of partially appropriate 4-tuples, the hypnotist may trigger them, thereby creating a unified new 4-tuple, the one desired by the client. In our experience, when this approach to change is used, it is essential that the hypnotist test his work thoroughly. In the example, we have been using, the author who had worked with the client and established the 4-tuple, turned control over the established anchors for the newly created 4-tuple over to the client and excused himself. After the client had been sitting by herself for several minutes in the office, another of the authors (older than the woman client who entered the office) asked the client where the author was. When she replied that she didn't know, he immediately attacked her verbally in a vicious manner. Her initial response was to reverse breathing, pale and begin to apologize; however, her right hand crept down to her knee (where the anchor for the newly created 4-tuple had been established) with typical unconscious movement. Once her hand had made contact with her knee, her entire communication shifted—she became assertive; her voice tone, tempo and melody, her body posture and gestures . . .all changed to the values of the 4-tuple she and the first author had created. In the midst of the continuing quarrel she glanced down, noticing her hand grasping her knee firmly and giggled. She then stood up, brushed by the second author with an amused smile and left the office in high spirits. This technique for testing the effectiveness of a newly constructed 4-tuple—we call it living metaphor (it will be discussed in detail in volume III of *Patterns of the Hypnotic Techniques of Milton H. Erickson, M.D.*) is only one of a number of techniques to insure that the work done in altered states and in the rather restricted context of an office transfer with full force to the client's coping patterns in the world of everyday experience.

Tracking model III is also an excellent choice for trance inductions with naive clients. Either the client is consulted directly or the hypnotist uses his own personal experience to discover, access and anchor portions of the client's past 4-tuples which in combination constitute the desired 4-tuple—deep trance. Since the hypnotist and the client are simply earnestly discussing these matters in a harmless conversation, there typically will be no recognition on the client's part that an induction is in progress until the deep trance (the desired 4-tuple) is an accomplished fact. The hypnotist using the 4-tuple model to organize his experience is systematically working through each of the variables in the 4-tuple, accessing and anchoring the portions of the client's past 4-tuples which most closely approximate the values of the variables in the desired 4-tuple.

In the context of communicating hypnotically with a client, one of the most important pieces of information you can come to detect is whether the client is congruent about the task you've engaged in. In the event that the client is congruent—all the messages carried by the client's body posture, gestures, tonality, tempo, syntax, words, breathing, . . . are consistent—

$$C (A_d < A_t, O, K, V >) \text{------> yes}$$

you have available in the 4-tuple a plethora of choices about how to proceed. The three tracking models presented in this section, while very powerful, represent only the simplest applications of the 4-tuple model.

In communication with congruent clients the hypnotist/communicator himself will most effectively communicate congruently to both the client's conscious and unconscious minds. This, of course, still allows the hypnotist/communicator many interesting choices about how to organize his communication. One such interesting choice revolves around the question of whether the hypnotist desires to be overt or covert in his communication. For example, in the context of trance inductions the hypnotist may choose to be overt, announce his intention to assist the client in entering an altered state. He may even describe to the client how he will proceed. The hypnotist then proceeds to induce trance with multiple messages in all channels each supporting and reinforcing the others. For example as he says,

> . . . *and your hand is beginning to lift . . .*

his voice rises in pitch as he says the word *lift*. He simultaneously lifts his own hand slightly with movements typically of unconscious responses. If the hypnotist is making contact with the client on his knee with his other hand, he may press down slightly on the client's knee just before he says *lift* and then release that pressure as he says the word *lift*. In this way he communicates consistent and reinforcing multiple messages in the A_d, A_t, K and V channels simultaneously.

The hypnotist/communicator may choose a covert induction with a congruent client. In this case, he arranges his communication somewhat differently. He may in communication with a congruent client who is attending to the language and visual dimensions of the hypnotist's communication; that is:

$$R (A_d < A_t, O, V, K >) ----> (A_d, V)$$

talk to the client about hypnosis and the multitude of ways which are available for him to assist the client in going into a deep trance. As he does this, he matches his body movements (detected visually by the client) to the words and sentences he presents. At the same time, the hypnotist/communicator marks out kinesthetically (hand pressure on the client's knee, for example) and with tonal and tempo shifts portions of the verbal message for special attention (see *Patterns*, volume I, analogue marking) to the client's unconscious mind; that is since

$$-R (A_d < A_t, O, V, K >) ----> (O, K, A_t)$$

the portions of the verbal message marked in the K and A_t

systems will be accepted and responded to by the client without any awareness. Thus the client inexplicably finds himself going into a deep trance in the middle of a discussion. Again, such maneuvers are what has traditionally been called magic.

Meaningful Communication in Hypnosis with Incongruent Clients

As we stated previously, there are two types of incongruity that we as hypnotist/communicators will typically encounter: that of simultaneous incongruity — the situation where the client offers in his or her communication, a set of messages which are inconsistent where the message carried by the client's voice tone (A_t), for example, fails to match the messages carried by the client's words (A_d), or the messages carried by the client's body posture, breathing rate or body movements (K detected by the hypnotist in his V system) or any of the other output channels the client is using to express himself. In the visual representation we have been developing,

$$C \,(\, A_d^{<} A_{t'}, K, V, O^{>}) \;\text{-----}\!> \text{no}$$

The second case is that of sequential incongruity — where the client is congruent at one point in time, t_1, and again at some later point in time, t_i. However, when the message value of the two 4-tuple from t_1 and t_i are compared, they are inconsistent with one another:

$$\overline{C} \,(\, C\,(A_d^{<} A_{t'}, K, V, O^{>})_{t_1}, (C\,(A_d^{<} A_{t'}, K, V, O^{>})_{t_i} \;\text{-----}\!> \text{no}$$

where

$$C\,(\, A_d^{<} A_{t'}, K, V, O^{>})_{t_1} \;\text{---------}\!> \text{yes}$$

and

$$C\,(\, A_d^{<} A_{t'}, K, V, O^{>})_{t_i} \;\text{-----------}\!> \text{yes}$$

In our experience, one of the most useful maneuvers that a hypnotist/communicator can make when faced with sequential incongruity is to convert it initially into simultaneous incongruity. One of the fastest and easiest ways to accomplish this is anchoring. Specifically, the hypnotist/communicator can anchor (either overtly or covertly) either of the parts which are expressing themselves incongruently overtime (sequentially) and then access the other one. Once the second one is accessed and is being expressed by the client, the hypnotist/communicator uses the anchor aleady established for the first part. One rather typical outcome of this maneuver is a profoundly altered state of consciousness as the client experiences the two incongruent parts simultaneously. The maneuver has always in our experience created (minimally) a state of profound confusion. The alert hypnotist can then easily utilize the resulting confusion state to track to a profound trance. We assume for the remainder of this section that the hypnotist is dealing with a simultaneously incongruent client.

Perhaps the most efficient method of presenting the set of choices which our models offer for effective and creative hypnotic communication with incongruent clients is for us to simply state that all of the patterns presented in volume I and up to this point in volume II of the *Patterns* series apply with full force to the incongruent client if the hypnotist/communicator regards each of the parts (represented by one of the sets of consistent messages presented) of the client to be a separate and congruent client. In other words, you as a hypnotist/communicator can accept each of the messages which you receive from an incongruent client as a valid representation of that human being as respond to each with the same principles and patterns which you would use toward a separate congruent client. Thus, for example, if one set of messages from the incongruent client is carried by the words (A_d), another by the body movements (K) and a third by the tonal and tempo patterning of the client's voice (A_t), you would apply that very same initial pattern that we have urged over and over again — meet the client at his model of the world — specifically, you would respond to each of the client's parts in the representational system and output channels you received the messages from them in. When you next replied to the client, your words would match in content the sense of the words (A_d) he had offered you while at the same time your voice tone and tempo

(A$_t$) qualities would approximate those you had received from him and your body movements (K) would be a response to those he had offered you in his previous communication. This simple application of the pacing technique of matching representational systems will guarantee that you will not encounter resistance. Resitance is simply a signal that the hypnotist/communicator has failed to pace some part of the client. By accepting each of the parts of the incongruent client as a valid representaton of that human being and by responding to each with the same care and with the same patterns you would use with individual clients, you proceed rapidly to come to be trusted by each of those parts, and resistance is impossible. This is an explicit representation of one of Erickson's famous double and triple takes.

One way to organize your thinking about how to respond to an incongruent client is to consider the whole continuum of possible responses you have as a communicator in that particular situation. At one end of the continuum of possible responses is what therapists call meta.-commenting. For example, with an incongruent client who states the words "Oh, yes, I'm ready to go into a deep trance," while simultaneously shaking their heads from side to side, meta-commenting would consist of the communicator saying something like, "I heard you say that you are ready to go into a deep trance and as you said that I noticed that your head was slowly shaking from side to side, . . . I'm a little confused. Could you help me with understanding what you really want?" At the other end of the continuum is a mirroring response; that is, the communicator responds by saying, "Oh good, I'm glad that you are ready," while simultaneously shaking his head from side to side. The first possibility is typical of what is commonly called insight or conscious mind therapy. It has the effect of forcing into the client's conscious awareness some portion of their communication which had been outside of consciousness until the communicator's meta-comment. The typical response is one of shock. It fails to respect the channels of communication which the client is selecting (both consciously and unconsciously) to communicate the various parts of himself. The second response — that of mirroring — is in our experience more typical of hypnotic communication, especially that of Milton H. Erickson. As communicators, we believe that there are no mistakes in communication — there are simply outcomes. The outcome of meta-commenting is shock value and the bringing into consciousness of material/parts that the client was previously unaware of. The outcome of mirroring is an immediate effective pace of all parts of the client expressing themselves and the avoidance of resistance. Our personal preferences run to what we consider the more graceful choice — that of mirroring. We all three maintain the choice of using either as the context dictates. Since this is a volume on hypnosis, the choices of responding to incongruent clients we will concern ourselves with are those located toward the mirroring end of the continuum. For these readers who are interested in developing a wide range of choices of response which cluster around the meta-commenting end of the continuum, we have created a model of a number of them in part II of volume II of *The Structure of Magic* (Grinder and Bandler).

The first, and in our experience, one of the most powerful of the choices of a hypnotic response to an incongruent client is the one already mentioned — mirroring. In order to be an effective mirrorer, the hypnotist/communicator must train him or herself to have a full range of choice about controlling his or her verbal and non-verbal output channels. The ability to provide an adequate mirroring response presupposes that the hypnotist/communicator has the ability to detect incongruency in order to be able to mirror it. The gracefulness with which the hypnotist/communicator adopts the particular patterns of incongruent cmmunication offered by the client will determine how effective this response. In teaching this response in our training seminars, we have the person learning to mirror copy the client in only one output channel at a time until they have developed their ability and confidence in that ability to gracefully alter their own communication until it matches the communication patterns of the client. One of the most frequent outcomes that the people we have trained in our seminars elicit when initially developing their skills in this type of response is that of accessing into consciousness in the client some other part or model of the world — usually one which is radically inconsistent with the previous one. We have called this the polarity, and the entire maneuver, playing polarity (see *The Structure of Magic*, volume II, part II.) For those of you familiar with the work of John Rosen, you will recognize this as one of the patterns he uses very effectively with schizophrenia. As an acquaintance of ours once stated: "Rosen so effectively meets the client at his (the client's) model of the world that he (Rosen) ruins the client's psychosis." The difference between these two outcomes (each an excellent choice yielding a useful outcome) is the subtleness with which the communicator adopts the patterns of incongruent communication offered by the client. If the maneuver is carried out with subtleness, the outcome is an immediate and profoundly effective pace. If the client detects in consciousness the maneuver, the outcome will be a rapid access into the client's behavior of some part of him which was previously outside of consciousness — the polarity maneuver.

Another choice of responding to incongruent clients is that offered by any of the covert induction techniques we have presented earlier. For example, the hypnotist/communicator may choose to question the client closely about his understanding of what a deep trance would be like (working his way systematically through the variables of the 4-tuple). As he does so, he is alert to note the responses by the client and to covertly anchor the responses which in combination will yield the type of altered state which will be useful for the purposes of the hypnotic encounter. The client, of course, is conscious only that he is having a harmless conversation with the hypnotist. Once the components of the altered state the hypnotist desires have been solidly anchored, he need only trigger the anchors for the components simultaneously, and the altered state will result. In making a choice about which system to anchor in, the 4-tuple and its associated R operator provide the hypnotist communicator with a principled and effective way of deciding — specifically, with incongruent clients, anchor in any system which is ~R. Another excellent choice with incongruent clients is to converse comfortably with the client about a relatively harmless topic while marking analogically certain portions of the verbal communication for special attention at the unconscious level. Again the R operator indicates which system to use for the marking of verbal messages — that is, any of the ~R systems. A third class of covert inductions which are effective with incongruent clients are those involving the intersecton of TOTEs as detailed in tracking model II. In using this model with incongruent clients the hypnotist/communicator may usefully select 4-tuples which involve TOTEs where the intersection occurs in one of the ~R systems. For example, if you as a hypnotist were working to get eye closure with an incongruent client whose R operator was V using tracking model II, you might have a conversation which included a discussion of among other things: watching a sunrise, diving into cold water, walking down a dusty, dirt road with a lot of traffic on it. Visually (the client's consciousness) these 4-tuples have very little in their intersection but kinesthetically, each includes a TOTE which leads in the direction of eye closure.

Another excellent choice is responding to incongruent clients is the surprise induction. The fact that a client is incongruent is a signal that he or she is not unified to their ability to respond. You may utilize this by creating a situation where they experience confusion. The client's being unable to act in a unified manner insures that their recovery from this state of confusion will take some time. There are many classes of surprise inductions. We suggest that you discuss earnestly with the client the issue which he is incongruent about. Once he is expressing the incongruency strongly, you need only detect any repetitive pattern of movement in the client and interrupt it. The handshake interruption induction we discussed at the beginning of this volume is the paradigm example. The handshake is, in this culture, an automatic response which is experienced as a single unit of behavior in consciousness. Its interruption leaves the client momentarily without a program — a state of confusion insues which can then be utilized to induce any useful altered state. Any repetitive motor patterns presented by the client offers the same opportunity to the alert hypnotist/communicator.

The choice of using metaphor with incongruent clients is one of the most powerful in our experience, especially the technique of stacked realities — these patterns are the subject of volume III of the Patterns series. Finally, we mention the choice of re-framing, either metaphorical or literal. This is an extensive area containing many interesting patterns some of which will be contained in a forthcoming publication (*Neuro-Linguistic Programming I*).

Each of the choices mentioned above as a creative and effective response to incongruent clients are formal patterns — patterns of process. As such the offer the hypnotist/communicator a potentially infinite number of specific choices in his or her response to those clients who come seeking assistance and who are incongruent.

Summary

One of the skills which most distinguishes Milton H. Erickson, M.D., of Phoenix, Arizona from other practitioners of hypnosis and the art of change has been his world reknowned ability to succeed with "impossibles" — people who have exhausted the traditional medical, dental, psychotherapeutic, hypnotic and religious avenues for assisting them in their need, and have not been able to make the changes they desire. One characteristic of such clients (both from the descriptions Erickson has offered to us and from our own experience with our "impossible" practice) is that they seem to be quite incongruent. They typically seek help, demanding or begging that they receive the assistance they verbally claim to want, yet there are portions of their behavior available to the astute communicator which indicate that there are parts of these clients (typically, outside of their consciousness) which have needs, desires and goals different from those presented verbally.

There are many ways to characterize those unique features of the fine human being Milton H. Erickson, M.D. of Phoenix, Arizona which account for this phenomenal ability. The two volumes of *Patterns* series constitute one such attempt; Jay Haley has offered another, *Uncommon Therapy*. We have stated repeatedly throughout this series that the patterns which we presented in our model are simply one way of organizing the vast and fascinating world of Ericksonian communication—as such, they can be evaluated most appropriately in our understanding by their usefulness in making available the same powerful hypnotic communication skills possessed by Erickson. Thus, they represent a set of choices *to be learned* and *used* by you as a practitioner in order to determine through your own experience how useful these models are for your work. Our experience of Erickson as well as our experience in utilizing the many learnings we have from him in our own work leads us to identify two characteristics which Erickson possesses which we believe accounts for much of his phenomenal success:

> (1) Erickson believes that the resources which the client needs to effect the change he desires are already available within him.

> (2) Erickson accepts and utilizes all communication/ behavior presented by his clients.

We wish to add that we also have found it extremely useful to incorporate these two beliefs as presuppositions of our communication and behavior.

Notice that given these two beliefs as presuppositions of communication and behavior in the hypnotic encounter, many of the otherwise unconventional patterns of Erickson's behavior follow quite naturally. Consider the first of these—if this is a presupposition of hypnotic communication, then the relevant question becomes how specifically to access those resources and to turn control of them over to the client either at the conscious or the unconscious level of functioning. In the *Patterns* series, we have identified a number of such techniques: the verbal patterns explicitly presented in volume I, the powerful patters of the 4-tuple, transderivational search, anchoring...in *Patterns II*. The second of the two beliefs we have identified—that of accepting and utilizing all the behavior presented—leads naturally to two questions: first, how to detect the communication/behavior being presented by the client; and secondly, how to utilize such communication and behavior once detected. Essentially the answer to the first question is the communication strategy—the the answer to the first question is the communication strategy we have referred to in this book as the up-time strategy—the communication strategy by which the communicator/hypnotist uses his 7 ∓ 2 chunks of attention to detect externally generated sensory experience—more specifically, the communication behavior of the client. This strategy allows him to detect the messages being offered by the client. There are particularly useful classes of messages which the effective and creative communicator/hypnotist will find useful: information which allows him to determine which portion of the world of potentially infinitely rich sensory and internally generated experience the client has an awareness of — the client's R-operator. This can be effectively and comfortably accomplished by the communicator/hypnotist by training himself to hear predicates which indicate representational system. The second useful class of messages offered by the client are these which allow the hypnotist/communicator to identify how the client is creating/organizing his or her experience — the client's L operator. Again, this can be easily accomplished by learning to see the accessing cues used by the client which indicate which lead system the client is using at a point in time. The third class of messages which will become available to the communicator/hypnotist operating with an up-time strategy is those which allow him to know whether the messages which the client is offering are consistent or inconsistent with one another — the client's C-operator. These three pieces of information are crucial to the art of graceful, effective and creative communication and change.

Suppose the client's C-operator is yes—that is, the messages offered in response to the communicator/hypnotist are consistent with one another. At that point in time, the communicator/hypnotist who also knows the client's R-operator, has a broad spectrum of choice of techniques to access and utilize the client's resources: the R-operator overlap principle, the tracking and sequencing of 4-tuples technique...

Suppose that the client's C-operator is no — that is, the messages offered by the client are inconsistent. It is precisely here that the powerful techniques offered by the 4-tuple model become particularly useful. Consistent with Ericksonian principle of accepting and utilizing all communication/behavior, the hypnotist /communicator accepts all the conflicting messages as valid representations of potentially powerful parts of the client. The client with his limited ability to represent in consciousness his ongoing experience, including his own communication behavior, will be aware also of only a portion of the multi-messages which the hypnotist/communicator uses in responding to the multi-message offered by the client. In general, the hypnotist/communicator will accept and respond to the portions of the client's unconscious communication in such a way as to remain outside of the client's consciousness, thus preserving the choice offered by the client, the hypnotist/communicator effectively paces all the models of the world the client as the first movement in successful hypnotic communication. By this relatively simple device, the term "resistant" client becomes unnecessary. This is, of couse, a simplified review of some of the major patterns offered up to this point in this volume — the use of multi-message communication requires a learning process just as does any complex skill. This is the structure of the phenomena referred to by Erickson as the "double take" and the "triple take".

The final section of this book is essentially as integration of the explicit techniques offered by the 4-tuple and its operators. It consists of two previously unpublished transcripts of Erickson working with the two clients who have come to him for psycho-therapeutic help. The films/videotapes from which these transcripts are taken are available as *The Artistry of Milton H. Erickson, M.D.* from Herbert S. Lustig, M.D., Ltd., P.O. Box 261, Haverford, PA 19041. We have organized the transcript into three columns: the first column presents the actual work done by Erickson with the clients. The second column presents what we refer to as the mini-patterns—essentially the verbal patterns identified and presented in this volume of *Patterns.* We strongly urge that you secure copies of *Artistry of Milton H. Erickson, M.D.* They are excellent in quality and together with the commentary which constitutes the bulk of the remainder of this volume of *Patterns,* they represent a powerful set of resources for developing your gracefulness, effectiveness and creativity in using the Ericksonian techniques. We recommend that you study these patterns carefully, selecting one or two of them for intensive use for several days at a time until they become part of your systematic, unconscious communication. At the end of the transcripts, we compare them, identifying and presenting the next higher level of patterning — the patterns, for example, of the sequencing of 4-tuples (one example of an Ericksonian tracking mode) as Erickson demonstrates his grace and power in accepting, utilizing all communication/behavior and accessing the appropriate resources in these two clients to assist them in the process of change.

Footnotes

Part 1, Patterns II

1. We suggest to the readers who sincerely desire to make these patterns of behavior part of their communication repertoire that they select one or two of the patterns presented each day and practice detecting and utilizing these patterns until they understand the outcome or consequences of the use of such patterns. Once you have gone through this procedure, the patterns will drop into unconscious behavior leaving you free to detect and utilize a new set. During the period of time when you are practicing these patterns, utilize your own most highly valued representational system as an aid in training yourself.

2. We recommend Gregory Bateson's excellent article concerning difference, Form, Substance and Difference in *Steps to an Ecology of Mind*, pages 448-466 (Ballantine Books, New York, 1972).

3. The term *a bit of information* has a well-defined technical meaning (see any presentation of Information Theory).

4. The alert reader will have noticed that having both the $\left\{ {i \atop e} \right\}$ superscript and the time/space subscript on the variables involves a certain amount of redundancy. Specifically, whenever the superscript on a variable is e, then necessarily the time/space coordinate is now/here. In other words when a person is attending to sensory experience (experience generated externally), they are experiencing sensory distinctions which are taking place at the present time and place. It is only in the case that the superscript on the 4-tuple is i, that the time/place coordinates could be other than now/here. Thus, a less redundant representation (and therefore, more elegant by modeling criteria) would simply use time/space coordinate subscripts: if no subscripts appeared on one of the variables of the 4-tuple, by convention, that variables would be assumed to be now/here. We have preserved the redundancy in the 4-tuple presented in the text as we have found it useful pedigogically in instructing people in the use of the 4-tuple in our workshops and seminars to use both of these representations.

5. Another way of understanding the up-time strategy in terms of the 4-tuple model is that the person operating out of the up-time strategy has introduced a constraint on his R operator. Specifically, this constraint can be thought of as a filter such that he is aware of, represents in consciousness, only externally generated experience. We can represents this visually as

$$R^e \ (A_d^{\leq}V, K, A_t, O^>)$$

This representation suggests that a person operating out of the uptime strategy may or may not be generating experience internally. In either case they have organized themselves so that they bring into consciousness only the portion of their experience which is externally generated. This is more congruent with our experience in using and teaching up-time strategy. Our thanks to Paul Carter for pointing this out as well as other comments.

6. This is a representation of the Whorf-Sapir hypothesis regarding the influence language systems have on the perception and experience of the users of the language systems involved.

7. A complete model of how to identify and utilize form patterns of verbal communicaton in order to assist a client in connecting language representations with experience.

8. Another way of understanding the way that the A_d and R operators interact is to assume that the R-operator applies first to the 4-tuple (primary experience):

$$R < V, K, A_t, O > \text{-----} > (V)$$

yielding, for example, the result that the client is at that point in time attending the visual dimensions of the experience. Then, once this has occurred, the client represents (to himself and to others) the portion of experience he is aware of in language forms.

$$A_d \ (R < V, K, A_t, O >) \text{-----} > A_d (V)$$

If the A_d and R operators are applied in this order, then the 4-tuple serves as a model for production of linguistic forms. Specifically, this explains how people who consistently attend in consciousness to the visual dimension of experience typically use predicates which presuppose a visual representation of experience. Thus when the 4-tuple model is being used for the purposes of a model of how people represent which portion of the messages which they receive from some other person, then it is useful to apply the R operator to the entire unit.

$$A_d<V, K, A_t, O>$$

That is,

$$R \,(A_d<V, K, A_t O>)$$

If, however, the 4-tuple model is being used for the purposes of understanding the relationship between a person's most highly valued representational system and the language forms they select (unconsciously) and use in their verbal communication, then the order of application which is most useful is

$$A_d \,(R<V, K, A_t, O>)$$

PART II

Transcript I

The following previously unpubished transcripts and commentary demonstrates Milton H. Erickson's combination of hypnotic and psychotherapeutic techniques. The transcripts illustrate Erickson's exquisite and systematic use of language patterns as well as the refined way these lower level patterns are grouped in order to effectively access and utilize the client's own resources in trance induction and utilization. These technical skills make his work powerful, effective, and subtle. It is useful to remember that Erickson is acutely sensitive to non-verbal communication, and is adroit in his use of such communication.

Monde is 32 years old, married and the mother of three children. She has had three therapy sessions with Erickson during the six months preceding, and proved to be an excellent hypnotic subject, demonstrating her ability to carry out deep trance phenomena. Her major concern was her insecurity about herself as a person, wife, and mother.

Nick is 20 years old and single, he has had no previous experience with hypnosis or psychotherapy. His only experience with Erickson occurred the day before the session presented here, in a social setting. Nick volunteered as a demonstration subject. Erickson's work with Nick is as systematic as his work with Monde.

The following transcripts contain three levels of patterning:

1. Verbal patterns outlined in Volume I of *Patterns of Hypnotic Techniques of Milton H. Erickson, M.D.*, by Richard Bandler and John Grinder.

2. Second level patterns of accessing and utilizing the client's own past experiences, the 4-tuples which contain the resources each of the clients needs to make the changes he desires. Essentially, this level of patterning is the grouping of the first level patterns into natural classes for the purposes of trance induction and utilization. For example, the first level patterns of deletion, cause-effect linguistic causal modeling, nominalization, conversational postulate, missing referential index...combine to form instructions for the client to employ the higher level patterns of transderivational search as an integral part of the hypnotic session.

3. Third level patterns of the sequences of the 4-tuples. One delightful result of applying the 4-tuple model to reach a deeper understanding of Erickson's work is that the two transcripts which appear and sound so different have a parallel (isomorphic) structure at this third level of patterning. This very powerful level of patterning therefore provides the hypnotist with an explicit overall formal strategy for organizing their hypnotic communication. This level of patterning will be discussed separately at the conclusion of the transcript and commentary on the first two level patterns.

Transcript I

E:

(1)	(1)	(1,2,3)
Well, Monde, this time, I'd like to have you take your time about going into a trance.	presupposition: . . . *this time . . . take your time about going . . .*	Transderivational search to past trance experience with verbal lead.

(2)	(2)	
I don't want you to go into a trance too soon.	presupposition: *...into a trance too soon.*	

(3)	(3)	
And you know how easy it is for you. (E turns to N)	mind reading: . . . *you know* . . .; presupposition: . . . *know* . . ., . . . *how easy* . . . ; missing referential index: *it;* causal modeling conjunction: *And you know* . . .	

(4)	(4)	(4,5,6)
And while Nick is here, I'd like to have you *watch* how Monde's face.	causal modeling - conjunction: *And while Nick* . . ., implied causative: . . . *while.* sentence fragment: . . . *I'd like to have you watch how Monde's face.;* embedded command: . . . *watch how Monde's* . . .	Transderivational search to clients (M) past trance 4-tuple instructing (N) to use visual lead: pacing observable and non-observable behavior.

(5)	(5)	
And your unconscious mind will *learn* a great deal.	causal modeling - conjunction: *And your* . . .; embedded command: . . . *learn a great deal.* nominalizations: *mind, deal;* presupposition: . . . *learn . . . a great deal.*	

(6)

So *turn* and *look* so you can see her.

(E turns to M)

(6)

causal modeling implied causative: *...So turn...,* embedded command: *... turn and look...*

(7)

Not quite that fast, Monde.

(7)

presupposition: *. . . that fast, . . . quite that fast.;* deletion: *what not quite.*

(7,8,9)

Fractionation and building of response potential (instructing clients (M) to not experience the accessed 4-tuple fully yet).

(8)

Let's have a little talk first, 'cause in the trance I will want you to do something of importance for you.

(8)

nominalizations: *talk, trance, importance;* presupposition: *. . . first. . . . . . in trance.* missing referential index: *. . . something of importance . . .*

(9)

And just for you.

(9)

presupposition: *. . . just . . . ;* deletion: *what just for you?;* casual modeling - conjunction: *And...*

(10)

And just waiting.

(10)

causal modeling - conjunction: *And . . .* presupposition: *. . . just. . ;* mind reading: *. . . waiting. . . ;* deletion: *who's waiting for whom/ what?* sentence fragment: *And just wait.*

(10 - 14)

Pacing clients (M) observable and non-observable behavior.

(11)

And you know why I'm waiting for.

(11)

causal modeling - conconjunction: *And you. . .;* sentence fragment: *And you know why I'm waiting for.;* mind reading: *. . . you know. . . ;* deletion: *. . . waiting for what?*

(12)

That's right. (M's face flattens)

(12)

missing referential index: *That's. . . ;* deletion: . . . *right for whom/what?*

(13)

That's right.

(13)

missing referential index: *That's. . . ;* deletion: . . . *right for whom/what?*

(14)

All the way shut. (M's eyes close)

(14)

deletion: . . . *what all the way shut:. . .,* presupposition: . . . *all the way. . . ,* sentence fragment: . . . *all the way shut . . .*nominalization: . . . *way. . .*

(15)

Now go deeply into trance, so that your unconscious can *deal* with that vast store of memories that you have.

(15)

presupposiiton: . . . *deeply. . . , . . . memories that you have. . . ; . . . vast. . . ,* nominalizations: . . . *trance, store, memories, unconscious. . . ,* causal modeling - implied causative: . . . *so. . . ,* embedded command: . . . *deal with that. . .*

(15 - 17)

Instructs client to attend to K variable (R-operator) of accessed 4-tuple: Polarity Move.

(16)

And I'd like to have you *feel* very comfortable.

(16)

causal modeling - conjunction: *And. . . ,* presupposition: . . . *comfortable. . . , . . . very comfortable. . . ;* embedded command: . . . *feel very comfortable. . .*

(17)

(17)

And while you're in the trance, I would like to have you *feel* the coolness, not too cold, but just coolness—just enough coolness so that you might want it to get just a bit warmer.

causal modeling - conjunction: *And. . . ,* implied causative: *. . . while. . . , . . . so. . . ,* presupposition: *. . . while you're in. . . , . . . not too. . . , . . . just. . . , . . . just. . . , . . e- nough. . . , . . .just. . . , . . . a bit. . . ,* deletion: *. . . too cold for what/ whom?. . . ., . . .a bit warmer compared to what/whom?. . . ,* nominalizations:. . . *trance, coolness, coolness, coolness. . . ,* missing referential index: *. . . it. . . ,* embedded command: *. . . feel the coolness. . .*

(18)

(18)

(18-22)

Now, while you *go* deeper and deeper into the trance, it is as if you're traveling a highway, passing this scene, that scene, in your life.

nominalizations: *. . . trance, scene, scene, life . . . ,* casual modeling - implied causative: *. . . while. . . ,* ambiguity scope: *. . . in your life. . . ,*presupposition: *. . . deeper and deeper. . . ,* missing referential index: *. . . it. . . , . . . this scene. . . , . . . that scene. . . , . . .a highway. . . ,* embedded command: *. . . go deeper. . . ,* unspecified verb: *. . . traveling. . . , . . . passing. . .*

Pacing age regression instructing client to attend to visual variable (R-operator) of accessed 4-tuple begins metaphor.

(19)

(19)

And perhaps something very nice that you could recall that you haven't thought about for years.

causal modeling - conjunction: *And. . . ,* missing referential index: *. . . something very nice . . . ,* sentence fragment: *And perhaps. . . for*

years, unspecified verb:
. . . recall. . . , . . .
thought. . .

(20)

And I think it'd be most interesting if you would *find* some childhood, infantile memory that you haven't thought of for years—such as the time when you discovered you could stand up and the entire world looked different.

(20)

causal modeling - conjunction: *And. . . , . . . and. . . ,* missing referential index: *. . . it. . . some childhood, infantile memory that. . . ,* presupposition: *. . . most interesting. . . ,* nominalization: *. . . memory. . . ,* causal modeling implied causative: *. . . such as. . . ,* missing referential index: *. . . the time. . . ,* unspecified verb: *. . . discovered. . . ,* presupposition: *. . . you discovered. . . ,* deletion: *. . . looked different to whom/different how? . . . ,* presupposition: *. . . looked different. . . ,* nominalization: *. . . world. . .*

(21)

The world suddenly takes on a wonderful *look* when you stand up and are no longer creeping.

(21)

nominalization: *. . . world. . . ,* unspecified verb: *. . . takes on. . . ,* presupposition: *. . . takes on. . . ,* embedded command: *. . . takes on a wonderful look when . . . ,* presupposition: *. . . stand up. . . ,* implied causative: *. . . when . . .*

(22)

And, older, you bent over and looked at the world from between your legs,

(22)

causal modeling - conjunction: *. . . and. . . ,* deletion: *. . . older than whom? . . .*

(23)

so you would *have* another view of this world look, that you looked at and found so interesting.

(23)

causal modeling implied causative: ...*and*..., ...*so* ..., embedded command: ...*you would have...* *view.* . . ., unspecified verb: . . . *have.* . . . , referential index: . . . *this world look.* . . , nominalization: . . . *world look.* . . , unspecified verb: . . . *found.* . . . , deletion: . . . *found interesting how:.* . . presuppostions: . . . *would have.* . . , . . . *you looked at.* . .

(24)

I would like to have you *single out* some one thing that you could talk to me about, that you could talk to strangers about, that you could *share.*

(24)

embedded command: ... *single out...thing...,* missing referential index: ...*thing...,* unspecified verb: ...*single out...,* implied causative: ...*that* ..., ...*that...,* ...*that...,* embedded command: ... *you could share...,* unspecified verb: ...*share...*

(24 - 26)

Instruction to access (transderivational search) past pleasurable 4-tuple (kinesthetic variable - R-operator).

(25)

Something very pleasing, very charming.

(25)

sentence fragment: *something...,* ...*charming...,* referential index: ...*something...,* presuppositions: ...*very...,* ... *very...,*

(26)

And just as you're spreading a feeling of cool comfort, you can *spread* a feeling of warmth and comfort over your experiences, 'cause they do radiate.

(26)

implied causative: ...*and just as...,* presupposition: ...*spreading...,* embedded command: ... *you can spread...,* unspecified verb: ...*radiate ...,* ...*spread...,* nominalization: ...*feeling...,*

...experiences..., selectional restriction: ... *spread feeling...over experiences...,* deletion: ... *do radiate what/to whom?...*

(27)

(27)

(27)

Now you *remember* watching Nick's (husband) hands lift upward.

embedded command: *Now you remember. . . lift upward. . .,* unspecified verb: . . . *remember. . .,* presupposition: . . . *remember. . .,* deletion: . . . *lifted up when/where?. . .*

Access (transderivational search—L-operator [V]) 4-tuple tracking to arm levitation.

(28)

(28)

(28)

I wonder if you know which of your hands is going to move up toward your face? . . .

presupposition: . . . *if you know. . .,* unspecified verb: . . . *know. . . move. . .,* presupposition: . . . *move. . .,* embedded question: . . . *I wonder. . . which. . . hands. . .*

Instructions to overlap from V variable of accessed 4-tuple to K variable (R-operator). Pacing observable behavior continued arm levitation.

(29)

(29)

29 - 35)

And I have that doubt, it's going to lift and *move* rapidly, up toward your face.

implied causative: . . . *and. . .,* nominalization: . . . *doubt. . .,* missing referential index: . . . *its. . .,* embedded command: . . . *its going to lift and move. . .,* verbs: . . . *lift and move . . .,* presuppositions: . . . *rapidly. . .*

Pacing observable and non-observable behavior continued arm levitation.

(30)

(30)

You're just beginning to know which one it is, since you're not going to be too sure until it's off your thigh.

presupposition: . . . *know. . .,* missing referential index: . . . *which one. . .,* . . . *it. . .,* implied causative: . . . *since. . .,* presupposition: . . . *not be sure. . ,*

implied causative: . . .
until. . . , referential index: . . . *its.* . .

(31)

(31)

Up it comes. Faster.
And faster. (M's left
hand and forearm lift
slightly) Now you
know. And it's pleas-
ing to know.

missing referential index:
...*it*..., unspecified verb:
...*comes...,* ...*know..,*
deletion: ...*know what?*
..., implied causative: ...
and..., presupposition:
...*to know...,*

(32)

(32)

And it's something
like that feeling—up
toward your face—
that feeling when
once before in your
infancy you discover-
ed your hand belong-
ed to you.

implied causative: ...
And..., missing referential index: ...*its...some-
thing...that feeling...,*
nominalization: ...*feel-
ing...,* missing referen-
tial index: presupposi-
tion: ...*discovered...,*
...*once before...,* un-
specified verb: ...*discovered...,* ...*like...*

(33)

(33)

And a nice thing to
learn—up toward your
face.

implied causative: *And.*
. . . , missing referential
index: . . . *thing.* . . ,
embedded command: . .
. *thing to learn.* . . , unspecified verb: . . . *to
learn.* . . , presupposi-
tion: . . . *learn.* . . , deletion: . . . *learn what?*

(34)

(34)

And your uncon-
scious is showing
that jerky movement,
because your uncon-
scious has allowed
your conscious mind
to use fluid move-
ment;

implied causative: ...*and
...,* missing referential
index: ...*that...move-
ment...,* cause effect: ...
because..., nominaliza-
tions: ...*unconscious...
conscious mind...,*
...*movement...,* presup-

position: ...*use...*, unspecified verb: ...*use...*
...*showing...*

(35)

(35)

and your unconscious
does it in this more or
less reflex-like way.
(M's left hand and
forearm continue to
lift slowly)

implied causative: . . .
and. . . , nominaliza-
tion: . . . *unconscious*
. . . , missing referential
index: . . . *it*. . . , unspecified verb: . . . *does*
. . . , presupposition:
. . .*does it in this*. . .*way*
. . .

(36)

(36)

(36 - 38)

And sooner or later, I
don't know just when,
you will *be wondering*
about something that
you would like to *see*.

implied causative: . . .
And. . . , embedded
command: . . . *will be
wondering*. . . , unspecified verb: ...*will be
wondering*. . . , missing
referential index: . . .
wondering. . . , missing
referential index: . . .
something. . . , embed-
ded command: . . . *you
would like to see*. . . ,
presupposition: . . .
would like to see...

Access (transderivation-
al search V-variable L-
operator) 4-tuple to age
regression and positive
hallucination.

(37)

(37)

I don't know if you
can open your eyes
and see it; maybe
you'll see it with your
eyes closed.

embedded question: . . .
I don't know. . . *open
your eyes*. . . , conjunction: . . . *and*, missing
referential index: . . . *it*
. . . , . . . *it*. . . , . . . *it*
. . . , presupposition: . .
. . *open eyes*. . . , . . .
see it. . . , . . . *with eyes
closed*. . .

(38)

(38)

A something you have
not seen for a long
time that pleased you

missing referential index:
. . . *something*. . . , presupposition: . . . *haven't*

then, and which you have forgotten about.

seen. . . ; unspecified verb: *. . . pleased. . . ,* presupposition: *. . . pleased. . . ,* missing referential index: *. . . then . . . ,* implied causative: *. . . and. . . ,* presupposition: *. . . have forgotten. . . ,* unspecified verb: *. . . forgotten. . .*

(39)   (39)   (39 - 41)

I talked with a young woman the other night and she's *know* what that good feeling was.

missing referential index: *. . . young woman. . . other night. . . she's. . ,* embedded command: *. . she's know what that good feeling was. . . ,* nominalization: *. . . good feeling. . . ,* unspecified verb: *. . . know. . . ,* presupposition: *. . . know. . .*

Metaphor continuation (from 18) access (transderivational search L-operator V) to 4-tuple age regression and pleasant memory (R-operator K)

(40)   (40)

She was holding her dog, and that was before she went to school.

missing referential index: *...She..., ...that..., ... she...,* implied causative: *...and...*

(41)   (41)

And some of the hopes that you had (E applies slight upward pressure to the sides of Monde's right wrist) in your childhood. (M's right hand and forearm lift)

implied causative: *. . . and. . . ,* missing referential index: *. . . some . . . ,* nominalization: *. . . hopes. . . ,* unspecified verb: *. . . had. . . ,* presupposition: *...had in your childhood...,* sentence fragment: *...and some...,* ...child-hood...*

(42)   (42)   (42 - 44)

And going to *touch* your face; and when it touches your face you won't be able to keep

Conjunction: *. . . And . . . ,* embedded command: *. . . going to touch your face. . . ,*

Pacing (L operator V) access 4-tuple of limited vision and negative hallucination.

your left, your right hand in that position.	cause effect: . . . *and when. . . you won't be able. . .* , missing referential index: . . . *it.* . . , presupposition: . . . *won't be able.* . . , missing referential index: . . . *that position.* . .

(43)   (43)

You can't put it down now, your left hand has to touch your face first . . .Up it goes.	presupposition: . . . *can't put it down.* . . , unspecified verb: . . . *can't put,* missing referential index: . . . *it.* . . , presupposition: . . . *has to touch...,* cause effect: *...has to..., first...,* presupposition: *...up...*

(44)   (44)

Now you and I can be all alone here. That's alright. And I can talk to anybody I wish.	presupposition: ...... *all alone...,* unspecified verb: *...can be...,* conversational postulate: ... *can be all alone here...,* implied causative: *...and ...,* missing referential index: *...anybody...*

(Turns to Nick)

(45)   (45)   (45 - 49)

And Nick, I don't want you to go into a trance just yet. But your unconscious mind is learning a great deal right now;	conjunction: *...and...,* presupposition: *...just ..., ...yet...,* unspecified verb: *...go...,* nominalization: *...unconscious mind...,* presupposition: *...a great deal...,* unspecified verb: . . . *is learning . . . ,* deletion: . . . *is learning what?...*	Pacing observable and non-observable behavior continued arm levitation.

(46)   (46)

only you don't know just what it is learning.	presupposition: *...just ...unspecified verb: . . . don't know...,* missing

referential index: ...*it*...,
presupposition: ...*is
learning*..., unspecified
verb: ... *is learning*...,
deletion: ...*what?*...

(47)

I'll tell you one of the things you're learning.

(47)

missing referential index: ...*one thing*..., presupposition: ...*you're learning*..., unspecified verb: ...*you're learning*...

(48)

And that is that your left hand is beginning to lift without your intention.

(48)

implied causative: ...*and* ..., presupposition: ...*is* ...*is beginning to lift*..., unspecified verb: ...*is beginning*...

(49)

And now your eyelids are showing you difficulty, and your face is smoothing out.

(49)

implied causative: ...*and* ..., unspecified verb: ... *are showing*..., presupposition: ...*are showing* ..., implied causative: ... *and*..., unspecified verb: ...*smoothing*..., presupposition: ...*smoothng*...

(Turns to Monde)

(50)

And while I've been talking elsewhere, Monde, you've been going deeper and deeper asleep.

(50)

implied causative: ...*and while*..., missing referential index: ...*elsewhere* ..., presupposition: ... *have been going*..., unspecified verb: ...*have been going*...

(50 - 67)

Pacing—arm levitation (L-operator - V) to age regression 4-tuple (R-operator K)

(51)

And now let's get that left hand up to your face so that your right hand can *go down*.

(51)

conjunction: ...*And*..., unspecified verb: ...*get* ..., cause effect: ...*so that*..., embedded command: ...*right hand can go down...,* unspecified verb: *...go...,* presupposition: *...go..., ...get*

(52)

(52)

Closer and closer. It's only about three inches; two and three quarters. (M smiles) That's right, you enjoy that.

presupposition: *closer closer...,* deletion: *...what's closer...,* missing referential index: *...its ...,* presupposition: *...only...,* unspecified verb: *...is...,* missing referential index: *...that...,* presupposition: *...is right...,* unspecified verb: *...is...,* presupposition: *...enjoy...,* unspecified verb: *...enjoy...,* missing referential index: *...that..., ...only...*

(53)

(53)

And it can come to you as a surprise when your right hand knows before you do just when your face is touched by your left hand.

conjunction: *...and...,* missing referential index: *...it...,* presupposition: *...can come...,* unspecified verb: *...can come...,* conversational postulate: *...and it can come to you as a surprise...,* cause effect: *...when...,* selectional restriction: *...right hand knows...,* unspecified verb: *...knows ...,* presupposition: *...knows...,* presupposition: *...knows...,* presupposition: *...is touched...,* conversational postulate: *...your face is touched...*

(54)

(54)

Closer and closer.

presupposition: *...closer and closer...,* deletion: *...what's closer to what? ...*

(55)

And maybe you can do a bit of cheating, only you don't know what I mean. That's right, you're beginning the cheating.

(55)

conjunction: ...*and*..., presupposition: ...*can do*...,* unspecified verb: ...*can do*..., conversational postulate: ...*do a bit of cheating*..., missing referential index: ...*bit of cheating*...

(56)

Only you don't know what I mean;

(56)

presupposition: ...*don't know*...,* unspecified verb: ...*don't know*...,* deletion: ...*what*...

(57)

but your unconscious does, and I'll identify it for you.

(57)

implied causative: ...*but your*..., nominalization: ...*unconscious*...,* presupposition: ...*does*...,* unspecified verb: ...*does* ..., ...*identify*...,* missing referential index: ...*it*...,* conjunction: ...*and*...,* ...*identify*...

(58)

You're moving your head so slightly downward to meet your hand. (M smiles)

(58)

presupposition: ...*are moving*...

(59)

And I hope you enjoy it as much as I wish.

(59)

conjunction: ...*and*...,* presupposition: ...*enjoy* ...,* unspecified verb: ...*enjoy*...,* missing referential index: ...*it*...,* implied causative: ...*as much as*...

(60)

And you probably will enjoy it more than I can know.

(60)

conjunction: *...and...,* presupposition: *...will enjoy...,* unspecified verb: *...will enjoy..., ...know...,* missing referential index: *...it...,* implied causative: *...more than...*

(61)

How's it going to culminate:

(61)

missing referential index: *...it...,* presupposition: *...going to culminate...,* unspecified verb: *...going...*

(62)

your head going to move down and *touch* your hand, your hand going to move up and *touch* your face?

(62)

embedded question: *... head going to move down and touch your hand?...* presupposition: *...going to move...,* unspecified verb: *...going to move...,* embedded command: *...touch your hand...;* presupposition: *...touch...,* unspecified verb: *...touch...*

(62a)

embedded question: *... hand...move up...face ...,* presupposition: *... going to...,* unspecified verb: *...going...,* embedded command: *...touch your face...,* deletion: *...touch where?...,* presupposition: *...touch...*

(63)

You really don't know, but you're going to find out.

(63)

presupposition: *...don't know...,* unspecified verb: *...know...,* implied causative: ...*but*..., presupposition: ...*find out* ..., unspecified verb: ... *going*..., sentence fragment.

(64)

(64)

Now which is it going to be?

presupposition: ...*going to be*..., unspecified verb: ...*going to be*..., missing referential index: ...*it*..., deletion: ... *which is what going to be?*...

(65)

(65)

Now you thought for a moment it'd be your hand.

presupposition: ... *thought*..., unspecified verb: ...*thought*..., missing referential index: ...*it*...

(66)

(66)

Still thinking it's your hand—

presupposition: ...*still thinking*..., unspecified verb: ...*thinking*..., deletion: ...*who's thinking about what?*..., sentence fragment.

(67)

(67)

and when it touches, your right hand will drop. (M's left hand and face touch; her right hand returns to her thigh)

implied causative: ...*and when*..., missing referential index: ...*it*..., presupposition: ...*touches* ..., unspecified verb: ... *touches*..., presupposition: ...*will drop*..., unspecified verb: ...*will drop*..., deletion: ... *touches where, when?*...

(68)

(68)

(68 - 72)

And very deeply.

sentence fragment: Deletions: ...*very deeply what/where?*...

Positive hallucination instructions for V/K disassociation.

(69)

Now somewhere out of the past you'll come upon a happy scene.

(69)

missing referential index: ...*somewhere*..., presupposition: ...*will come*..., unspecified verb: ...*come*..., unspecified verb: ...*come*..., deletion: ...*scene of what/whom?*... missing referential index: ...*a happy scene*..., nominalization: ...*scene*...

(70)

And I want you to *visualize* it. A happy scene.

(70)

conjunction: ...*And*..., embedded command: ...*want you to visualize it*..., presupposition: ...*visualize it*..., missing referential index: ...*it*..., sentence fragment. missing index: ...*a happy scene*..., deletion: ...*visualize what/whom/where?*...

(71)

And just *reach* in and *take* it and *bring* it forth.

(71)

conjunction: ...*And*..., selectional restriction, embedded commands: ...*reach in...take it... bring it*..., presuppositions: ...*reach, take, bring*... missing referential index: ...*it, it*..., deletion: ...*for whom/what?*...

(72)

You don't have to have everything, just the happiness.

(72)

presupposition: ...*have* ..., unspecified verb: ...*have*..., missing referential index: ...*everything* ..., nominalization: ... *happiness*...

(73)

Let's see if you can open your eyes a little bit, and *be alone* with me.

(73)

conversational postulate: *...let's see if you can...bit...*, presupposition: *...open...*, unspecified verb: *...open...*, implied causative: *...and ...*, embedded command: *...be alone with me...*, presupposition: *...be alone...*, unspecified verb: *...be alone...*

(73 - 81)

Maintain V/K disassociation 4-tuple reference for limited vision, positive and negative hallucinations. (L operator V)

(74)

And where we are isn't important. (M partially opens her eyes)

(74)

conjunction: *...and...*, deletion: *...important to whom?...*

(75)

You remember last time—you knew that you were *seeing* everything.

(75)

presuppositions: *...you remember...*, unspecified verb: *...remember...*, referential index: *... last time — ...*, presupposition: *...knew...*, unspecified verb: *...knew ...*, embedded command: *...were seeing everything...*, presupposition: *...were seeing...*, missing referential index: *... everything...*

(76)

But you saw that videotaping, a scene that you didn't remember—

(76)

implied causative: *...But ...*, missing referential index: *...that videotaping, a scene...*, presupposition: *...didn't remember...*, unspecified verb: *...remember...*

(77)

(77)

how Herb held up a sign for me to read; and you didn't see it at all.

missing referential index: ...*a sign...*, deletion: ... *when?...*, conjunction: ...*and...*, presupposition: ...*didn't see...*

(78)

(78)

And I want your attention just on me, while you sense and *see* that scene from the past.

conjunction: ...*And...*, nominalization: ...*attention: ..., scene..., ...past ...*, deletion: ...*attention on me how/when?...*, implied causative: ... *while...*, presupposition: ...*sense...*, unspecified verb: ...*sense...*, presupposition: ...*see...*, missing referential index: ... *that scene...*, deletion: ...*whose past? ...*embedded command: ...*see...*

(79)

(79)

Your head will move back so you can look at me. (M's head moves upward and backward, her eyes open fully and gaze toward E, and her left hand remains elevated near her face)

presupposition: ...*will move back...*, deletion: ...*when...*, implied causative: ...*so...*

(80)

(80)

And you're going to go through a learning experience, and *see* just me.

conjunction: ...*And...*, presupposition: ...*going to go...*, unspecified verb: ...*go...*, nominalization: ...*experience...*, embedded command: ... *see just me...*, missing referential index: ...*a learning experience...*

(81)

And that's all. You hear my voice. And now will come to your mind some very nice, happy experience out of your childhood.

(81)

conjunction: ...*And...*, missing referential index: ...*that's...*, deletion: ... *all...what?...*, presupposition: ...*hear...*, conjunction: ...*and...*, presupposition:...*will come* ..., unspecified verb: ... *will come...*, missing referential index: ...*some very happy experience* ..., nominalization: ... *experience...*, *childhood* ..., presupposition: ... *out of your childhood...*

(82)

And I tell you to describe it.
M: Splashing in the water.
E: Splashing in the water?

M: A lake.
E: Tell me more about it.
M: I'm doing so with total abandonment.
E: You what?
M: I'm playing with total abandonment.
E: A total abandonment. And where is the water? Or don't you really know yet?
M: It's a lake, not the ocean. And I'm very small.
E: Would you say you're three feet tall? Or don't you even know what three feet means?
M: I'm about two years old.
E: Oh, two years old.

(82)

conjunction: ...*And...*, presupposition: ...*describe...*, missing referential index: ...*it...*

(82)

Dialogue

Pacing

(83)

Now was two-year-old Monde having a very good time?

(83)

unspecified verb: ...*having*..., missing referential index:...*a very good time*...

Instructions to client (M) to attend to V variable (R-operator) of accessed 4-tuple then overlap (R operator) to K variable. Continued metaphor meta instructions.

(84)

And memorize all those good feelings, because there's a lot of them.

(84)

conjunction: ...*And*..., unspecified verb: ...*memorize*..., missing referential index: ...*all those good feelings*..., nominalization: ...*feelings*..., presupposition: ...*there's*..., missing referential index: ...*them* ..., cause-effect: ...*because*...

(85)

It's a learning.

(85)

missing referential index: ...*it's*..., ...*learning*..., nominalization: ...*learning*...

(86)

Just as learning an alphabet and learning to recognize letters and numbers is the basis for an entire future of reading, writing, enumerating,

(86)

implied causative: ...*just as*..., presupposition: ...*learning an alphabet*..., unspecified verb: ...*learning*..., missing referential index: ...*an alphabet...letters...numbers*..., unspecified verb: ...*recognize*..., deletions: ...*reading, writing, enumerating what?* ...

(87)

so are the good feelings of splashing with total abandonment in water—

(87)

selectional restriction: implied causative: ...*so* ..., missing referential index: ...*good feeling*..., deletion: ...*whose feelings of*..., nominalization: ...*total abandon-ment*...

(88)

(88)

something that you *learn* and will stay with you in later life to be used in a direct-ed fashion.

missing referential index: ...*something*..., embed-ded command: ...*some-thing that you learned*..., unspecified verb: ...*learned*..., pre-supposition: ...*you learned and will stay*..., referential index: ...*later life*..., unspecified verb: ...*used*..., presupposi-tion: ...*to be used...fash-ion*..., missing referen-tial index: ...*directed fashion*..., nominaliza-tion: ...*fashion*..., dele-tion: ...*who/how used learning?*...

(89)

(89)

(89 - 92)

And now I'd like to have you *see* yourself over there, (E briefly points to M's left; she looks toward her left)

causal modeling con-junction: ...*And*..., em-bedded command: ...*see yourself over there*..., presupposition: ...*see yourself*..., missing re-ferential index: ...*over there*...

Instructs client (M) to access (L-operator - V) positive K 4-tuple at-tending (R-operator - V) to V variable, overlap (R-operator) to K vari-able; pacing.

(90)

(90)

doing something else, very charm-ing . . .

presupposition: ...*doing* ..., missing referential index: ...*something else* ..., unspecified verb: ... *doing*..., deletion: ... *charming to whom?*...

(91)

(91)

It'll *clear up*; you'll *see* it plainly.

embedded command: ... *clear up...see it plainly* ..., missing referential index: ...*it*..., presup-

position: ...*clear up...*,
unspecified verb: ...*clear up...*

(92)   **(92)**

Tell me what it is.
M: Chasing ducks.
E: Chasing a duck?
M: A group of ducks.
E: A group of ducks.
Now how do you
like the looks of
little Monde?
M: Very carefree.
E: What's that?
M: Very carefree.
E: Very carefree.

deletion: ...*tell when/to whom?...*missing referential index: ...*tell me what...it is...*

(93)   **(93)**   **(93 - 96)**

And that is something
that little Monde can
use in the years to
come, isn't it?

conjunction: ...*And...*, missing referential index: ...*that...*, ...*something ...*, embedded command: ...*Monde can use in years to come...*, unspecified verb: ...*can use ...*, presupposition: ... *can use...*

Meta instructions to anchor positive K variable of accessed 4-tuples for later use; continued metaphor. Tag-question (polarity).

(94)   **(94)**

And she needs to
learn that enjoyment.

conjunction: ...*And...*, embedded command: ... *needs to learn...*, presupposition: ...*needs to learn...*, unspecified verb: ...*to learn...*, missing referential index: ... *that enjoyment...*

(95)   **(95)**

'Cause along life's
highway are various
things and you need
to *learn* the things,

implied causative: ... *cause...*, nominalization: ...*life's highway...*, missing referential index: ...*various things...*, conjunction: ...*and...*, em-

bedded command: ...
*need to learn the things
...*, unspecified verb: ...
to learn..., presupposition: ...*need to learn...*,
missing referential index:
...*thing...*

(96)

(96)

and discover later
how you can use
those learnings. You
're not cold, are you?
M: No.
E: Comfortable?
M: Yes.
E: It's nice to be
comfortable, isn't
it?

conjunction: ...*And...*,
presupposition: ...*discover later...*, unspecified verb: ...*discover...*,
*discover when/where
/how?...*, presupposition: ...*can use...*, unspecified verb: ...*use...*,
missing referential index:
...*those learnings...*,
nominalization: ...*learnings...*, tag question: ...
are you...

(97)

(97)

(97 - 100)

Now, think of something bad, before the
age of six; and watch
yourself doing it,

presupposition: ...*think
of something bad...*, unspecified verb: ...*think
...*, deletion: ...*bad to
whom?...*, missing referential index: ...*something bad...*, conjunction: ...*and...*, presupposition: ...*watch yourself doing it...*, missing
referential index: ...*it...*

Instructs client (M) to
access (L-operator - V)
negative K 4-tuple, attending (R-operator) to
V variable; trade K value
of negative K 4-tuple for
previously anchored
positive K value. Pacing
tag question.

(98)

(98)

'cause before the age
of six you can't do
anything that's really
very bad.
M: Kicked in a window.
E: You what?
M: Kicked in a window.
E: Did you enjoy
kicking in that
window?

implied causative: ...*because...*, presupposition:
...*can't do anything very
bad...*, unspecified verb:
...*do...*, missing referential index: ...*anything
that's very bad...*, deletions: ...*bad to whom?*
...

M: I was shocked that it broke.
E: You were shocked that it broke.

(99)

It's nice to learn what a shock is, isn't it (M laughs)

(99)

tag question: ...*isn't it* ..., missing referential index: ...*it*..., ...*it's*..., unspecified verb:...*learn* ..., nominalization: ... *shock*...

(100)

And adult understandings are based on understandings that we get. How do you feel, being here and being there? (M looks to the left and then returns her gaze toward E)
M: It feels natural.
E: Quite natural. And how tall are you over there? (E briefly turns his toward M's left; M looks toward her left). . . . Where is the window?
M: It's a school window.
E: And where's the broken glass?
M: In the cafeteria.
E: Anybody around?
M: I was too young to eat lunch there, but the lunchroom's full of people. And I have on a red raincoat. And my mother's picking me up at 12 o'clock.
M: How hungry are you?

(100)

conjunction: ...*and*..., missing referential index: ...*there*..., ...*adult understandings*..., ...*understandings*..., deletion: ...*get from whom/ where?*..., unspecified verbs: ...*based*..., ...*get* ...

M: And I'm gonna be in trouble.

E: How hungry are you?

M: I'm not, I'm scared.

E: Real scared. Scared little Monde.

M: Yep.

(101)

E: And doesn't a small child's terror *look* differently than it really feels to the child?

(101)

conjunction: *...And...*, embedded command: *...small child's terror look differently than it really feels...*, missing referential index: *...small child's terror...it...the child...*, presuppositions: *...terror looks...*, nominalizations: *...terror...*

(101 - 102)

Instructs client (M) to access (L-operator - V) positive K 4-tuple attending (R-operator - V), overlap (R-operator - V) to K variable.

(102)

The child sees something very big, and you can smile about it.

(102)

missing referential index: *...The child...something very big...it...*, presupposition: *...child sees something...you can smile...*, conjunction: *...child sees...and...you smile...*

(103)

Now let's go to some happy thing when you were about 10 years old—something you forgot a long time ago . . . Going to tell me about it?

M: I caught my first fish.

E: How big was the fish?

M: It's a little sunfish.

E: A little sunfish.

(103)

missing referential index: *...Let's...some happy time...something...long time ago...*, *presupposition: ...let's go...you forgot...*, unspecified verb: *...go...*, *...forgot ...*, deletions:*...happy to whom?...*

(103 - 105)

Transderivational search (L-operator - V) to K variable of accessed 4-tuple, maintaining V/K disassociation.

(104)

(104)

Why didn't you show me how big the sunfish was? There's something strange, isn't there, about you right now? I can do this (E briefly holds his hands apart)

M: I feel very unattached to the rest of my body.

presupposition: *...why didn't you show me...*, missing referential index: *...There's something strange...*, tag question: *...isn't there...*, presupposition: *...something strange...about you...*

(105)

E: You're unattached to your body. (M looks toward E) In other words, would you like to see your adult body sitting (E briefly points to M's left; M looks toward her left) in that chair over there? And your unconscious mind over here, (E briefly turns his body to the left, points to M's left, and continues to point) but your body's over there? Tell me the position in which you're sitting. (E briefly turns his head toward M's left)

M: My feet are on the floor.

E: What's that?

M: My feet are on the floor.

E: Your feet are on floor, yes.

M: My toes are turned in.

E: (E returns his hands to the resting clasped position) Now I'd like to

M: I'm leaning to the left.

E: What's that?

M: I'm leaning to the left.

E: I'll tell you something else that's interesting—yes?

M: My hand is still up.

(105)

presupposition: ... *You're unattached...,* unspecified verb: *...unattached...,* presupposition: *...you like to see...,* nominalization: *...unconscious mind...,*

(106) (106) (106 - 107)

E: Your hand's still up; and now you know you can't put it down. (M laughs)

conjunction: *...and...,* presupposition: *...you know you can't put it down...,* unspecified verb: *...know...*

Pacing, arm levitation and dialogue.

(107) (107)

The only way you can put it down is if the right hand moves up at the same speed that the left hand moves down . . . Oh, you can try harder. (M looks toward E and then gazes to the left) than that (M laughs) —much harder. I want some action.

M: I think I'm too lazy?

E: What's that?

M: I think I'm too lazy.

E: You think you're too lazy?

M: I'm comfortable.

cause-effect: *...The only way you can...is if...,* presuppositions: *...you can put it down...right hand moves up...left hand moves down...,* unspecified verb: *...moves...,* embedded command: *...move up at same speed that...*

E: You're comfort-
able, very com-
fortable.
M: Yes . . .

(108) (108) (108 - 115)

E: That's way it's
nice to be, now,
in the future. At
the present time,
even though you
can't move your
hands except in a
certain way, you
can feel comfort-
able, can you not?
M: Yes.

missing referential index:
*...that's way...its nice...
in the future...in a cer-
tain way...*, implied
causative: *...even
though...* presupposi-
tion: *...it's nice...can't
move your hands except
...can feel comfortable
...*, unspecified verbs:
...moves...feel..., tag
question: *...can you not?*

Metaphor, meta-
instructions (R-operator
- K variable) for future
use. Polarity pace.

(109) (109)

E: And you could
feel comfortable
in a crowd? . . .

conjunction: *...And...*,
presupposition: *...could
feel comfortable...*, un-
specified verb: *...feel...*,
missing referential index:
...a crowd...

(110) (110)

I'd like to tell you
something. Every-
body is like his finger-
prints.

missing referential index:
*...something...every-
body...*, presupposition:
*...is like...fingerprints
...*, unspecified verb: *...
like...*

(111) (111)

They're one of a kind.
And never will be
another like you. And
you need to enjoy
always, being you.

missing referential index:
...they're one of..., deletion: *...to whom?...*, ...
conjunction: *...and...*,
missing referential index:
...another..., presupposition: *...need to enjoy...*,
unspecified verb: *...en-
joy...*

(112)

And you can't change it—just as fingerprints can't be changed.

(112)

conjunction: *...And...*, presuppositions: *...you can't change it...*, unspecified verb: *...change ...*, missing referential index: *...it...*, implied causative: *...just as...*, presupposition: *...fingerprints can't be changed...*, unspecified verb: *...changed...*

(113)

And I want you have that same secure feeling that you had when you were splashing in the water, when you caught your sunfish.

(113)

conjunction: *...and...*, presupposition: *...have same secure feeling... you had when you were splashing...*, unspecified verb? *...have...had...*, missing referential index: *...same secure feeling... splashing in the water...* nominalization: *...feeling...*, implied causative: *...when...*

(114)

That same secure feeling that you have even now when you can't move your hand, except in the way I defined.

(114)

missing referential index: *...that same secure feeling...*, nominalizations: *...secure feeling...*, presupposition: *...have even now...*, can't move your hand..., *unspecified verb: ...have..., ... move..., define..., implied causative: ...when...*

(115)

And you can *feel* comfortable anytime you wish. (M gazes toward E)

(115)

conjunction: *...And...*, embedded command: *... can feel comfortable...*, presupposition: *...can feel comfortable anytime you wish...*, unspecified verbs: *...feel..., ...wish*

..., missing referential index: ...*anytime*...

(116)

You think I ought to prove it to you? Alright.

(116)

mind reading: ...*you think I ought to*..., presuppositions: ...*to prove it*..., unspecified verbs: ...*think...prove*..., missing referential index: ...*it*..., deletion: ...*what's alright for whom?*...

(116 - 122)

Meta-instructions linking eye closure to negative K variable and eye opening to positive K variable.

(117)

As soon as you shut your eyes you'll begin to feel uncomfortable. (M's eyes shut)

(117)

cause-effect: ...*As soon as you'll feel*..., presupposition: ...*shut your eyes...you'll beging to feel*...unspecified verb: ...*feel*...

(118)

And you'll feel comfortable as soon as you get them open,

(118)

conjunction: ...*and*..., cause-effect: ...*you'll feel ...as soon as*..., presupposition: ...*you'll feel comfortable*..., *as you get them open*..., unspecified verb: ...*feel*..., missing referential index: ...*them*...

(119)

but you can't get 'em open right away. And you're really going to feel uncomfortable— very. (M winces) (M's eyes blink)

(119)

conjunction: ...*and*..., implied causative: ...*but you*..., presupposition: ...*can't get 'em open*..., missing referential index: ...*them*..., presupposition: ...*you're really going to feel*..., unspecified verb: ...*feel*...

(120)

(120)

Now (M's eyes open and gaze to left) you know what to do to feel comfortable; (M looks toward E) then you'll have more courage, won't you? (M smiles and looks toward left)

presupposition: ...*you know what to do to feel* ..., unspecified verb: ... *know...*, *...feel...*, missing referential index: ... *what to do...*, implied causative: ...*then...*, presupposition: ...have more courage..., *unspecified verb:* ...have..., nominalization: ...*courage...*, tag question: ... *won't you?...*

(121)

(121)

You felt uncomfortable, did you not? (M nods head vertically)

presupposition: ...*you felt...*, tag question: ... *did you not?...*deletion: ...*uncomfortable about?*

(122)

(122)

What (M looks towards E) did it feel like?

M: Like I just had (M shakes head horizontally, briefly closes her eyes, then gazes toward E) to move my hands.

E: As if you had to move your hand.

missing referential index: ...*what...it...*, deletion: ...*felt like to whom?...* presupposition: ...*felt...*

(123)

(123)

(123 - 131)

Now how about selecting something else that's even more uncomfortable?

presupposition: ...*how about selecting something...that's even more uncomfortable...*, missing referential index: ...*something...*, deletion: ...*more uncomfortable than what?/to whom?...*

Transderivational search (L-operator - unspecified) to negative K (R-operator) 4-tuple. Meta-instructions linking eye closure to negative K 4-tuple and eye opening to positive K 4-tuple; dialogue.

(124)

(124)

One of the worst things that you can think of.

missing referential index: *...One of the worst things...*, presupposition: *...you can think of ...*, unspecified verb: *... think...*

(125)

(125)

Close your eyes and feel that discomfort, knowing you can control it by opening your eyes.

presuppositions: *...close your eyes...feel...knowing you can control...*, missing referential index: *...that discomfort...it...*, unspecified verbs: *...feel ...knowing...*, nominalization: *...discomfort...*

(126)

(126)

Now first you *feel* it thoroughly, the most uncomfortable feeling you've ever had.

embedded command: *... first you feel it...*, presupposition: *...you feel it...the most uncomfortable feeling...*, unspecified verb: *...feel...*, missing referential index: *... it...*, the most uncomfortable feeling...,

(127)

(127)

Close your eyes and feel it . . . (M closes eyes)

presupposition: *...Close your eyes...feel it...*, unspecified verb: *...feel...*, missing referential index: *...it...*

(128)

(128)

And you can afford to suffer and feel miserable because you know that when you have really felt it thoroughly, you can open your eyes and banish it. . .

conjunction: *...and...*, presuppositions: *...you can afford to suffer and feel miserable...you know...*, *open your eyes and banish...*, unspecified verbs: *...afford..., ... feel..., ...know..., ...felt*

..., ...*banish*..., missing referential index: ...*feel it..., banish it...,* implied causative: ...*because...*

(129)

(129)

But really examine that uncomfortable feeling . . .

causal conjunction: ... *But...,* presupposition: ...*really examine...,* unspecified verb: ...*examine...,* missing referential index: ...*that uncomfortable feeling...*

(130)

(130)

That's not as threatening, really, as you thought . . . You're getting through it . . .

missing referential index: ...*that's...,* presupposition: ...*that's not as threatening...,* deletion: ...*threatening to whom?* ...mind reading: ...*as you thought...,* unspecified verb: ...*getting...,* missing referential index: ...*it...*

(131)

(131)

Have you had enough of it? (M smiles and nods head vertically) You (M opens eyes and looks to left) know what to do. Now I'd like to have you look at two-year-old Monde . . . What is she doing now?
M: Running.
E: Running? Now let's look at her with the ducks . . What's she doing?
M: Giving them breadcrumbs.
E: Giving them breadcrumbs. . . How plainly do you *see*

conversational postulate: ...*Have you had...,* missing referential index: *enough of it...,* presupposition: ...*you know...,* unspecified verb: ... *know...,* missing referential index: ...*what to do...*

the ducks?
M: They're very clear.
E: How many?
M: About twelve.
E: You say about twelve. Can you count to twelve?
M: (M laughs)...Can count to ten.

(132)

E: You count to ten. That's right. . . You can pretend anything and *master* it. . . Now that broken window—did your mother spank you?
M: Yes.
E: Close your
M: She made me pay for it.
E: Close your eyes.
M: Out of my allowance.

(132)

missing referential index: *...that's...*, deletion: ... *right for whom?...*, presuppositions: *...you can pretend... and master...*, unspecified verbs: *...pretend...master...*, missing referential index: *...anything...it...*, embedded command: *...master it ...*, sentence fragment: *...now that...*

(132 - 149)

Meta-instructions; trans-derivational search (L-operator - K; R-operator - K) to negative K 4-tuple; links negative K 4-tuple to eye closure; pacing; links positive K to eye opening; tag question tense change.

(133)

E: Close your eyes, (M closes eyes) feel that spanking right now. (M winces) . . . .Feel it very intensely...

(133)

presupposition: *...feel that spanking...feel it intensely...*, missing referential index: *...that spanking...it...*

(134)

That's quite some spanking, wasn't it? (M opens eyes, looks toward left, then toward E) . . .

(134)

presupposition: ... *that's quite some spanking...*, missing referential index: *...some spanking ...it...*, tag question: ... question: *...wasn't it...*, ungrammatical sentence...

(135)

How did it feel to be spanked? (M looks toward left)
M: It's worse before than it is during, (M looks toward E) or after. (M briefly closes eyes, smiles, and looks toward E)

(135)

presupposition: ...*feel to be spanked...*, missing referential index: ...*it...*, deletion: ...*spanked by whom?...*

(135a)

E: And while it's going on, you don't think you'll live through it, do you? (M laughs, and looks toward left) . . . Isn't it that way with all troubles?
M: Um huh. . . .

(135a)

causal conjunction: . . . *and while. . .* , presupposition: . . . *you don't think you'll live through* . . . , unspecified verbs: . . . *think. . . live.* . . , tag question: . . . *do you?.* . . , missing referential index: . . . *it that way. . . all troubles. . .* nominalization: . . . *trouble. . .*

(136)

E: But you did live through that spanking. . . And you can live through (M looks toward E) other troubles. . .

(136)

causal conjunction: ... *but...*, unspecified verb: ...*live...*, missing referential index: ...*that spanking...*, conjunction: ...*and...*, presupposition: ...*you can live* ..., unspecified verb: ... *live...*, missing referential index: ...*other troubles:* ...nominalizations: ...*troubles...*

(137)

How would you like another spanking? (M looks toward left, smiles, and shakes head horizontally).

(137)

conversatonal postulate: ...*How would you...*, deletion: ...*spanking by whom?*

(138)

Well, you're going to get another . . . (M looks toward E) And a very hard one. And you'll get it as soon as you *close* your eyes.

(138)

conjunction: ...presupposition: ...*you're going to get and a very hard one...,* missing referential index: ...*another...hard...one...,* conjunction: ...*and...,* presupposition: ...*you'll get it*..., unspecified verb: ...*get...,* missing referential index: ...*it...,* cause-effect: ...*as soon as...,* embedded command: ...*close your eyes...*

(139)

And you want to think they won't *close*.

M: (M looks toward left) No, I'd want to know who's going to spank me.
E: You want to know?

(139)

conjunction: ...*and...,* presupposition: ...*you want to thnk...,* unspecified verb: ...*won't think*..., embedded command: ...*close...*

(140)

You'll know when your eyes are closed ...It's going to be a hard spanking. (M looks toward E and then toward the left)

(140)

presupposition: ...*you'll know...,* unspecified verb ...*know...,* implied causative: ...*when...,* presupposition:...*going to be a hard spanking...,* deletion: ...*hard to whom?* ...*spanking by whom?*

(141)

And trying to avoid that spanking, your eyes are going to *close* and *stay closed.* Down go the lids. Now. (M's eyes close and she winces)

(141)

conjunction: ...*and...,* presuppositions: ...*trying to avoid...,* unspecified verb: ...*trying...,* missing referential index: ...*that spanking...,* embedded command: ...*eyes are going to close and stay closed...*, pre-supposition: *...going to close...stay closed...*

(142)

And there's gonna be some *hate* in you, for that spanking—hate and anger and pain...

(142)

conjunction: *...and...* presupposition: *...going to be hate, anger and pain...*, unspecified verb: *...going...*, nominalizations: *...hate... anger...pain...*, missing referential index: *...for that spanking...*, deletion: *...spanking by whom?*

(143)

And feel it all...(a tear begins to form in each eye)

(143)

conjunction: *...and...*, presupposition: *...feel it all...*, missing referential index: *...it all...*

(144)

And you're going to feel some "never a-again"...

(144)

conjunction: *...and...*, presupposition: *...you're going to feel...*, nominalization: *..."never again"*

(145)

And now you're going to feel "I can live through this, and never again will I have that spanking and that hate and that anger."...

(145)

conjunction: *...and now ...*, presupposition: *... you're going to feel "I can live"...and "never again will I have"...*, unspecified verb: *...live ...*, missing referential index: *...this...that... spanking...that hate... that anger...*, nominalizations: *...hate...anger ...spanking...*

(146)

(146)

And let your bottom be stinging — still stinging after you *open* your eyes . . . (M's eyes open)

conjunction: *...and...*, implied causative: *... after...*, presuppositions: *...bottom be stinging... still stinging...*, embedded command: *...open your eyes...*

(147)

(147)

And tell me about (M's eyes look toward right) the stinging feelings. (M's eyes look toward left) . . .

conjunction: *...and...*, presupposition: *...tell me about the stinging...*, missing referential index: *...the stinging feelings... by whom?*

(148)

(148)

You don't need to remember the incident, but you can *remember* the feelings. (M looks toward E, nods head vertically, and looks toward left) . . .

presupposition: *...don't need to remember...you can remember...*, unspecified verb: *...remember...*, nominalization: *...incident..., ...feelings...*, embedded command: *...you can remember the feelings...*

(149)

(149)

How does your bottom feel? (M looks toward E and then toward left)
M: Hurt from a hairbrush.
E: Like the hairbrush had been used.

presupposition: *...bottom feel?...*

(150)

(150)

(150 - 155)

Is it alright (M looks toward E) to tell me and strangers about the incident? (M looks toward left) . . .

conversational postulate: *...Is it alright to tell ...*, presupposition: *...tell me...*, missing referential index: *...strangers about the incident...*, nominalization: *...incident...*

Meta-instructions for future use of positive (anchored to eye closure and opening) K 4-tuple; amnesia; begin reintegration of all accessed 4-tuples; re-orientation to adult Monde.

(151)

Your unconscious knows all (M looks toward E) about it— probably more than your conscious mind does.

(151)

presupposition: ...*your unconscious knows... more than your conscious mind does...*; unspecified verb: ...*knows* ..., nominalizations: ... *unconscious...conscious mind...*, missing referential index: ...*about it...*

(152)

And your unconscious mind can *keep* from you, from your conscious mind, anything it doesn't want you to know consciously.

(152)

conjunction: ...*and...*, presupposition: ...*unconscious mind can keep from you conscious mind anything it doesn't wnat you to know...*, unspecified verbs: ... *keep...,* ...*know...,* missing referential index: ... *anything...,* nominalizations: ...*unconscious mind...,* ...*conscious mind...,* embedded command: ...*can keep from you...*

(153)

And that way you can *lessen* the pain. Is that agreeable? (M nods head vertically)

(153)

conjunction: ...*and...,* missing referential index: ...*that way...,* presupposition: ...*you can lessen...,* unspecified verb: ...*lessen...,* nominalization: ...*pain...,* missing referential index: ...*that* ..., deletion: ...*agreeable to whom?...,* embedded command: ...*can lessen the pain...*

(154)

And you can do that in the future. Or many things . . .

(154)

conjunction: ...*and...,* presupposition: ...*you can do that...,* unspecified verb: ...*do...,* missing referential index: ... *many things..., ...that in the future...,* nominalization: *...future...,* sentence fragment.

(155)

(155)

And now, two-year-old Monde, and the window-breaking Monde, and the duck-chasing Monde, duck-feeing Monde, grows up, into an adult Monde.
M: Not yet. (M looks to left)

conjunction: *...and...,* presupposition: *...two-year-old...window breaking...duck-chasing ...duck feeding...grows up..., adult Monte...,* unspecified verb: ... *grows...*

(156)

(156)

(156 - 165)

And she's going to *meet me.*

conjunction: *...and...,* embedded command: ... *she's going to meet me ...,* presupposition: ... *going to meet...,* unspecified verb: *...meet...*

Completes integration of all accessed 4-tuples; reorientation to adult Monde; tests anchoring linkage between eye opening and positive K 4-tuple.

(157)

(157)

Only the window-breaking, (M looks toward E) duck-chasing, water-splashing Monde doesn't know me . . . But the adult Monde does—

presupposition: *...window breaking...water-splashing Monde doesn't know...adult Monde does...,* unspecified verb: *...know...*

(158)

(158)

the one with secure feelings and comfort.

missing referential index: *the one...,* nominalization: *...feeling..., ...discomfort...,* presupposition: *...secure...*

(159)

(159)

Knowing that when discomfort *strikes* you, you can *close* your eyes and then *open* them.

presupposition: ...*knowing that...you can close ...then open...*, unspecified verb: ...*knowing... strikes...*, embedded commands: ...*when discomfort strikes...*, *you can close your eyes... and then open them...*, implied causative: ... *when..., ...then...*, nominalization: ...*discomfort...*

(160)

(160)

and show me how you'll behave when something makes you feel insecure or uncertain (M's eyes look toward left, slowly close, slowly open, and then quickly close)...

conjunction: ...*and...*, presupposition: ...*show me...you'll behave...you feel...*, implied causative: ...*when...*, missing referential index: ... *something...*, unspecified verbs: ...*show...behave...*

(161)

(161)

And you need all that time, do you? (M's eyes open and look toward left) . . .

conjunction: ...*and...*, presupposition: ...*you need all that time...*, unspecified verb: ...*need ...*, missing referential index: ...*all that time ...*, nominalization: ... *time...*, tag question: ... *do you?...*

(162)

(162)

Show me how quickly you can close (M looks toward E) your eyes and banish the discomfort.

presupposition: ...*show ..., how quickly...can close...and banish...*, unspecified verbs: ... *show...banish...*, missing referential index: ... *the discomfort...*, nominalization: ...*discomfort ...*

(163)

and open them with
the discomfort gone.
(M looks toward left,
and blinks slowly)

(163)

conjunction: ...*and*...
presupposition: ...*open
them..., discomfort gone
..., unspecified verb: ...
gone...,* missing referential index: ...*the discomfort...,* nominalization:
...*discomfort...*

(164)

You don't even have
to remember what
that discomfort was.
(M looks toward e)

(164)

presupposition: ...*even
have to...,* missing ref-
erential index: ...*that
discomfort...,* nominali-
zation: ...*discomfort...*

(165)

By the way, you're
comfortable?
M: Yes.

(165)

tag question: ...*by the
way, you're comfort-
able?...*

(166)

E: I'm going to a-
    waken you very
    shortly.

(166)

presupposition: ...*going
to awaken...,* missing
referential index: ...*very
shortly...*

(166 - 172)

Meta-instruction for fu-
ture pacing and testing
anchoring linkage (be-
tween arm movement
and positive K 4-tuple)

(167)

And I'm going to ask
of you something that
will cause you dis-
comfort. Briefly.

(167)

conjunction: ...*and...,*
presupposition: ...*ask of
you something...will
cause you...,* missing
referential index: ...
something...,* nominali-
zaton: ...*discomfort...,*
missing referential index:
...*briefly...*

(167a)

Will that be alright?
M: Yes.

(167a)

deletion: ...*alright for
whom?...*

(168)

E: I'll ask two things of you; will that be alright? (M nods head vertically) . . .

(168)

presupposition: ...*two things of you...*, missing referential index: ...*two things...that...*, deletion: ...*be alright for whom?* ...

(169)

After you're awakened, I want you to find out how horribly hot it is here—

(169)

implied causative: ... *after...*, presuppositions: *you're awakened...to find out...*, unspecified verb: ...*find...*

(170)

and how it's impossible for you to move your left hand . . .

(170)

conjunction: ...*and if...*, presupposition: ...*you'd like...be irritable... about it...*, unspecified verbs: ...*like...*,

(171)

And if you'd like to be irritable with me about it being so hot, will you do so?
M: Yes.

(171)

implied causative: ...*and if...*, presupposition: ... *you'd like...be irritable ...about it...*, unspecified verbs: ...*like...*, nominalization: ...*irritable ...*, tag question: ...*will you do so?...*

(172)

E: I'd enjoy having you *be irritable.* Now close your eyes. (M's eyes close)

(172)

presupposition: ...*you be irritable...close...*, unspecified verbs: ...*enjoy...be...*, embedded command: ...*be irritable* ...

(173)

Your unconscious mind has learned a lot—it knows it can function by itself.

(173)

presuppositions: ...*mind has learned...it knows... can function by itself...*, unspecified verbs: ...

(173 - 179)

Amnesia; meta-instructions; future pace; polarity pace.

*learned...knows...func-
tion...*, missing referential index: *...a lot...*,
nominalization: *...un-
conscious mind...*

(174)

(174)

Your conscious mind
can *learn* from it, can
use the learning that
the unconscious mind
has,

presupposition: *...can
learn...can use...learn-
ing that...mind has...*,
unspecified verbs: *...
learn...use...*, missing
referential index: *...from
it...the learning...*, nominalization: *...the learning...*, *...conscious mind
...learning, unconscious
mind...*, embedded com-
mand: *...can learn from
it...can use the learning
...*

(175)

(175)

as well as the learning
your unconscious
mind can reach back
into the past and sin-
gle out: any one thing,
two things, three
things—even twelve
ducks.

implied causative: *...as
well as...*, presupposi-
tions: *...can reach back
...single out...*, missing
referential index: *...the
learning...into the past
...one thing...two things
...three things...*, selectional restriction: *...
twelve ducks...*, nomi-
nalizations: *...learning
...things...unconscious
mind...*

(176)

(176)

I've given you a task,
two tasks. Discom-
fort, and an immobile
hand.

presupposition: *...given
you a task...two tasks...
discomfort...immobile
hand...*, unspecified
verb: *...given...*, missing
referential index: *...a
task...two tasks...*, nominalization: *...task...
tasks...discomfort...*

(177)

(177)

And which do you think you want to *banish* first? The discomfort or the arm?

conjunction: ...*and which...*, presupposition: ...*you think...want ...to banish...*, unspecified verbs: ...*think...want ...banish...*, missing referential index: ...*discomfort...*, nominalization: ...*discomfort...*

(178)

(178)

And you don't know; but your unconscious mind will let you find it out.

conjunction: ...*and...*, presupposition: ...*unconscious mind will let you find...*, unspecified verbs: ...*know...*, ...*find ...*, deletion: ...*know what...*, implied causative: ...*but...*, missing referential index: ...*it...*, nominalization: ...*unconscious mind...*

(179)

(179)

Now take it easily and comfortably, and a-waken. (M opens eyes, smiles, turns head to right and looks at E) Hello, Monde.
M: Hi . . . (M looks at her right arm, moves it and her trunk, and looks around) It's hot.
E: Any interest there? (M looks at E)
M: Hum?

unspecified verb ...*take ...*, missing referential index: ...*it...*, presupposition: ...*and awaken ...*, ...*easily...comfortab ly...*

(179a)

sentence fragment, missing referential index: ... *any...*, ...*these...*, nominalization: ...*interest...*

(180)

(180)

(180 - 190)

E: Have anything interesting there?
M: My hand?

unspecified verb: *have* ..., missing referential index: ...*anything inter-*

Polarity pace; test anchoring linkage between arm movement and posi-

E: Um huh.
M: It's sweating.
E: Sweaty. (M looks at her right hand)
M: Yeah, it's hot in here.

esting there..., deletion: *...interesting to whom?*

tive K 4-tuple by behavioral presuppositions.

(181)

(181)

E: It's hot. (M looks at and moves her right hand) . . . Which hand has the longer lifeline? (M turns her head to the left and right, looks at her right palm and laughs)
M: I don't know; I can't look at the other one. (M moves her head downward)

missing referential index: *...it's hot...*, deletion: *...hot for whom?...*, presupposition: *...which hand...*, unspecified verb: *...has...*

(182)

(182)

E: What do you mean, you *can't look* at the other one? Look me in eye and tell (M moves head upward and looks at E) me you *can't look* at the other one.

embedded commands: *...can't look...*, *can't look...*, presupposition: *...can't look...*, *can't look...*, missing referential index: *...other one...*

(183)

(183)

Do you expect me to believe that?
M: Yes, I expect you to . . . It's a very strange feeling. It's as if my other arm doesn't even belong to me, it's so light. It's just

missing referential index: *...that...*, unspecified verbs:*...expect...*, *...believe...*

hanging there
suspended from a
wire, it's not at-
tached.

(184)   (184)

E: It's unattached. It   missing referential index:
   is yours, isn't it?   ...*it's unattached...*, un-
M: I think so. (M   specified verb: ...*unat-*
   looks at left hand   *tached...*, presupposi-
   and then looks   tion: ...*it is yours...*,
   downward)   missing referential index:
                              ...*it...*, tag question: ...*is
                              it not?...*

(185)   (185)

E: When do you   presupposition: ...*you
   think you'll be able   think...able to move...*,
   to *move* it?   unspecified verb: ...
M: (M looks at E)   *think...*, embedded com-
   When *it* becomes   mand: ...*you'll be able
   uncomfortable.   to move it...*, missing
                              referential index: ...
                              move it...

(186)   (186)

E: When it becomes   missing referential index:
   uncomfortable . .   ...*it...there...*, unspecifi-
   (E turns head to   ed verb: ...*becomes...*
   his right, looks
   toward M's left,
   and then looks at
   M) Will you wheel
   my chair over
   there, please?
M: Put your chair? (M
   points to her left
   with her right
   hand) Shall I get
   up to move it?

(187)   (187)

E: I don't know of   unspecified verb: ...
   any other way.   *know...*, deletion: ...*any
M: (M stands up and   other way to do what?*

her left hand falls downward) I just moved my hand.

for whom?..., referential index: *...any other way ...*

(188)

(188)

E: You can move your hands. (M sits down, clasps hands together and looks at E) Is that the only way you can find out if you can move your hand?

M: Well, it didn't seem to respond too much. I—(M gestures with both hands) it was as if it wasn't part of me. It was very comfortable; it was fine left a-lone.

unspecified verb ...*find ...*, ...*move...*, missing referential index: ...*the only way...*, nominalization: ...*way...*

(189)

(189)

E: How very fine if left alone. How does your arm feel right now?

M: Normal.

E: Normal—no fatigue?

M: No.

E: Is it still hot here?

M: Yes, it's very hot. (M wipes her forehead with her left hand)

deletions: ...*what's fine/ who?...*, unspecified verb? ...*fine...*, ...*left...*, deletion: ...*what's fine?*

(190)

(190)

E: Well, don't worry, a cool breeze will come. All right.

deletion: ... *worry about?...*, ...*come from? ...*, unspecified verb... *come...*, ...*worry...*,

Transcript II

Transcript II

(1)

E: Did you know that you went into a trance while I was working with Monde?

N: No. I thought I did. I wasn't sure.

(2)

E: And this is the first time you've had any experience with hypnosis.

N: Yes.

(3)

E: So you're going to *find* a lot of new things out about yourself.

(4)

Only you'll really *know* what you're going to find out until after you have found out.

---

(1)

Implied Causative: *while*, nominalizations: *trance*, presuppositions: *know*.

(2)

Nominalizations: *experience, hypnosis*.

(3)

Implied causative: *so*, embedded command: *find a lot of...*, missing referential index: *things:* unspecified verb: *find...*, deletion: *new for whom?*

(4)

Sentence fragment: *Only you'll really know... until after...* Embedded command: *know what you'll* [*will*] Presupposition: *know*, missing referential index: *it, what you're* [*are*] *going...*, Implied causative: ... *until*, unspecified verb: *...know*, digital confusion.

(1-4)

transderivational search to Nick's previous trance 4-tuple; meta-instructions.

(5)	(5)	(5-8)
All you life you've known that you could *lift* your hand and lower it.	Unspecified verb: *known*, Embedded command: *lift your hand...*, Presupposiiton: *known ...you could...*, mind reading: *...You've known...*	suggests arm levitation; polarity move.

(6)	(6)	
But there's something you learned long ago, and that was that you couldn't lift your hand—	Polarity: *but*, referential index: *...something...*, presupposition: *...learned long ago*, presupposition: *...couldn't...*	

(7)	(7)	
that you didn't know it was your hand.	Missing referential index: *...it...*, mind reading: *...you didn't know...*, unspecified verb: *...know...*, presupposition: *...know...*	

(8)	(8)	
You were an infant, and your hands were just objects.	Presupposition: *...you were an...*,	

(9)	(9)	(9-16)
And one of the first things that a person does when he goes into a trance—he looks at some one spot.	Conjunction: *...and... he looks...*, missing referential index: *...he...*, missing referential index: *some spot, things*, unspecified verb: *does*.	pacing observable and non-observable behavior; suggests amnesia; transderivational search (L-operator and R-operator are K) to previous trance 4-tuple.

(10)	(10)	
He doesn't need to move, he doesn't need to do anything except let his unconscious mind *take over* and *do everything*.	Missing referential index: *...he*, deletion: *move where:* referential index: *he*, deletion: *talk to whom*, referential index: *he, anything*, dele-	

tion: *do anything how?/ to whom:* embedded command: *unconscious mind take over,* embedded command: *and do everything,* deletions: *who take over? take over what?,* referential index: *everything,* unspecified verbs: *take over, do.*

(11)

(11)

And the conscious mind doesn't have to do anything—it's usually not even interested.

Causal modeling conjunction: *and,* deletion: *whose conscious mind?* unspecified verb: *have to do,* deletion: *interested in what?* unspecified verb: *interested,* presuppositions: *have..., interested...*

(12)

(12)

And while I've been talking to you, you've altered your respiration, your heart rate is altered.

Causal modeling conjunction: *and,* implied causative, *while,* Presupposition: *altered,* unspecified verbs: *altered,* deletions: *altered how?*

(13)

(13)

I know from past experience that your blood pressure is changed, your pulse is changed, and your eyelid reflex is changed.

Mind reading: *I know from past...that you,* presuppositions: *changed...blood pressure, changed...pulse, changed...eye reflex.* In all three instances the verb *changed* is unspecified.

(14)

(14)

And you really don't need to keep your eyes open; but you can *close* them now...

Causal modeling conjunction: *and,* embedded command: *close them now,*

(15)

Yet a little flatter.

(15)

Presupposition: *yet*, presupposition: *...little flatter*, deletion: *what is a little flatter? for whom?* sentence fragment.

(16)

Is learning to *get* acquainted with yourself at another level of being.

(16)

Sentence fragment, deletion: *what is...?* unspecified verb: *learning*, unspecified verb: *get acquainted*, presupposition: *learning*, embedded command: *...get acquainted...*

(17)

Now first of all I'd like to have you *enjoy* the comfort.

(17)

Embedded command: *enjoy the comfort*, unspecified verb: *enjoy*, presupposition: *enjoy...*, nominalization: *...comfort...*

(17-18)

continue R-operator - K variable of ongoing 4-tuple digital confusion.

(18)

I'd like to have you discover that your sense of comfort continually increases.

(18)

Unspecified verb: *discover*, presuppositions: *discover, continually increases*, nominalizations: *sense, comfort.*

(19)

Now in the back of your mind, which is a common phrase, we know a lot of things;

(19)

Nominalizations: *back, mind*, selectional restriction: *which is a common phrase*, unspecified verb: *know*, referential index: *we, things*, deletion: *know a lot about what?* presupposition: *know...*

(19-22)

amnesia suggestions; mixing logical levels of communication ("...back of mind, which is a common expression...")

(20)

and sometimes we have trouble getting those things into the front of our mind.

(20)

Conjunction: *and*, referential index: *sometimes, we, those things*, unspecified verb: *have trouble, getting,* presupposition: *have trouble getting,* nominalization: *mind mind...trouble...*

(21)

(21)

We can have a name on the tip of our tongue, but we can't say it: we don't know what it is, but we know that we know it, but we just can't *think* of it, but it's there ready to be said.

Missing referential index: *a name,* presuppositions: *have, can't say, don't know, know, can't think,* embedded command...*think of it,* deletion: *ready to be said to whom?*

(22)

(22)

That's because the unconscious is hanging on to it.

Cause-effect: *that's because,* unspecified verb: *is hanging,* deletion: *hanging on to it for what?,* nominalization: *unconscious,* presuppoition: *is hanging on...*

(23)

(23)

(23-28)

And you know, of course, do you not, Monde, that you're in a trance too:

Presupposition: *know,* Tag question—polarity: *do you not,* presupposition: *you're [are],* nominalization: *trance.*

meta-instructions to both clients to utilize the succeeding experience.

(24)

(24)

Well enjoy the trance, and *intensify* all the learnings I started with you.

Presupposition: *enjoy,* unspecified verb: *enjoy,* nominalization: *trance,* conjunction: *and,* unspecified verb: *intensify,* nominalization: *learnings,* embedded command: *intensify the learnings...*

(25)

(25)

And whatever I say to him, you can *adapt* to yourself.

Causal modeling Conjunction: *...and...,* presupposiiton: *you can adapt,* unspecified verb: *...adapt...,* missing referential index: *...whatever..., ...to him..., embedded command: ... adapt...*

(26)

(26)

I might suggest that he *recall* a happy meal, and you might recall something else that's happy.

Unspecified verbs: *... recall..., recall,* presuppositions: *recall a happy meal, recall something else,* causal modeling conjunciton: *...and...,* missing referential index: *a happy meal, ...something...,* embedded command: *...recall...,* deletion: *...happy for whom?*

(27)

(27)

So you transform my words to him, so that they fit you as a person; and anything I say to you, he will fit to himself as a person.

Causal modeling implied causative: *So..., ...so that..., ...and...,* presuppositions: *...you transform my words..., they fit you..., he will fit...,* unspecified verbs: *transform, fit, fit,* missing referential index: *my words, ...they, ...anything.*

(28)

(28)

(28-34)

Now I know there is some reason why you came to Phoenix to *see* me.

Presuppositions: *...there is some reason why...,* missing referential index: *...some reason...,* mind reading: *I know...,* nominalization: *reason,* embedded command: *... see me...*

disassociation conscious /unconscious mind suggestion; organ language for arm leviation ("... handle...")

(29)

You had some purpose in mind, but exactly what that purpose was, I doubt if you had very much of an understanding.

(29)

Presuppositions: *you had some purpose...,* ... *you had very much...* unspecified verbs: *...had ..., ...doubt...had...,* missing referential index: *...some purpose..., that purpose, an understanding,* mind-reading sequence: nominalizations: *purpose, mind, purpose, understanding.*

(30)

Usually you don't know why, but your unconscious mind does *know* a great deal more.

(30)

Causal modeling: *...usually...but...,* presupposition: *...you don't know ..., ...mind does know ...,* missing referential index: *...a great deal...,* deletions: *more than what?,* embedded command: *...mind does know a great...* nominalizations: *unconscious mind.*

(31)

And you unconscious mind in knowing that additional material—

(31)

Sentence fragment: Causal modeling, conjunction: *And...,* presupposition: *...mind does know...,* unspecified verb: *knowing,* missing referential index: *...that additional material...,* nominalization: *...unconscious mind...*

(32)

and let it come to your mind slowly, gradually, In such a way that you're not disturbed, you're not distressed.

(32)

Causal modeling, conjunction: *...And...,* Presuppositions: *...let it come..., ...slowly, gradually..., ...in such a way ..., ...you're not disturbed..., ...not distressed...,*

unspecified verbs: ...
*come..., ...disturbed...,
...distressed...,* missing
referential index: *...it...,
...in such a way...,* deletion: *...disturbed by?...,
...distressed by?...*

(33)

(33)

(35-48)

in such a way that you
become aware that
you can *handle*
things, and *under-
stand* things,

Presuppositions: *in such
a way..., you become
aware..., you can handle
..., ...understand...,* unspecified verbs: *become
aware, handle, under-
stand,* missing referential
index: *in such a way, ...
things, ...things...,*
causal modeling-implied
causative: *...that?...,
...that?...,* and, em-
bedded commands: *...
you becomes aware...,
you can handle..., ...
understand...*

visual/kinesthetic disas-
sociation suggestions;
transderivation search
(L-operator is V) for
negative K 4-tuple tied
with reference 4-tuple
from day before.

(34)

(34)

and *discover* there are
some things you dis-
like and some that
you *like* and that there
are many different un-
derstandings that are
possible to you.

Causal modeling con-
junction: *...and..., and
..., and...,* presupposi-
tions: *discover..., ...
thing you dislike..., ...
some that you like..., ...
there are many..., ...are
possible to you...,* un-
specified verbs: *...dis-
cover, dislike, ...like...,*
missing referential index:
*somethings..., ...some
..., many different un-
derstanding...,* deletion:
...possible how?/when?,
embedded command: *...
and discover..., ...some
that you like...,* nomi-
nalizations: *...under-
standing...,*

(35)

(35)

Since this is really the
first time I've met

Implied causative: *...
since... but..., ...uncon-*

you, really talked to you, I can't really know very much a-about you, but your unconscious does know much more about you than you do.

scious does know much ..., ...than you..., unspecified verbs: *know..., ...than you...,* deletions: *...very much about what?, ...know much more about what? ... talk about what?,* missing referential index: *... very much..., much more...,* nominalization: *unconscious..., ... talk about?*

(36)

(36)

It's got a whole background of years of *learning*, feeling, thinking, and doing.

Presuppositions: *...got a whole background...of learning, feeling, thinking...doing...,* unspecified verbs: *got, learning, thinking, doing,* missing referential index: *Its..., ...background of years.,.*

(37)

(37)

And all of our days we are *learning* things—learning how:

Causal modeling conjunction: *...and...,* presuppositions: *...we are learning... learning how,* embedded command: *... we are learning...,* missing referential index: *all of our day, ...we..., things...,* unspecified verbs: *...learning... learning...*

(38)

(38)

how to *appraise them*, how to *assess* them, how to *feel* about them.

Presuppositions: *...how to appraise..., ...how to assess..., ...how to feel,* embedded commands: *how to appraise, how to assess, how to feel,* unspecified verbs: *appraise, assess, feel,* missing referential index: *...them..., ...them..., ... about them...*

(39)

And no matter how many good things occur in one's life, there are bad things, too.

(39)

Conjunction: ...*and* ..., presuppositions: ... *many good things occur, there are bad things too,* unspecified verb: *occur,* missing referential index: ...*good things..., one's life..., bad things,* deletions: ...*good for whom? ...bad for whom?,* nominalization: *life.*

(40)

And there's no way of escaping unpleasantness.

(40)

Conjunction: ...*and...,* presupposition: ...*no way of escaping,* unspecified verb: ...*escaping,* deletions: *no way for whom?* nominalizations: *way, unpleasantness.*

(41)

And you need to *learn* to *look* at things that are unpleasant—without fear, with a willingness to *understand*, and with a willingness to *learn* how well you can adjust.

(41)

Causal modeling conjunction: *And...,* Causal modeling, conjunction: ...*and...,* presuppositions: ...*need to learn..., to look at things..., ... without fear..., with a willingness to understand..., ...with a willingness to learn..., you can adjust,* unspecified verbs: ...*learn, understand, learn, adjust,* embedded commands: ... *learn to look..., ...under stand..., ...learn...,* deletions: ...*unpleasant to whom?/without fear of what/whom?,,* missing referential index: ... *things...,* nominalizations: *fear..., ...willingness..., willingness.*

(42)

(42)

And you do it without a sense of discouragement or fear...

Sentence fragment. Causal modeling, conjunction: ...*you do it...*, *without a sense of discouragement...*, *or fear*, missing referential index: ...*it...*, missing referential index: ...*it...*, nominalizations: ...*sense, discouragement, fear*, unspecified verb: ...*do...*

(43)

(43)

Now when you were introduced to me yesterday, you had a feeling of fear. You didn't really need that fear, but you had it.

Mind reading: *when you were introduced...you had a feeling of fear...*, presupposition: ...*you had a feeling...*, ...*didn't really need...*, *you had it* ..., unspecified verbs: ...*had...*, ...*need...*, ...*had...*, missing referential index: ...*a feeling of fear...*, ...*that fear...*, ...*it...*, nominalization: *feeling, fear*, causal modeling conjunction: ...*but...*, deletion: ... *fear of whom/what? ... feelings of what?* embedded command: ...*know.*

(44)

(44)

It's nice that you did have a feeling of fear, because you need to *know* all the feelings that you have.

Presupposition: ...*nice that you did have a feeling...*, ...*need to know all...*, ...*feeling that you have...*, unspecified verbs: ...*have...*, ...*know...*, ...*have...*, missing referential index: ...*It's nice...*, *a feeling...*, *all the feelings...*, nominalizations: ...*feeling...*, ..., *fear...*, ...*feelings* ..., embedded command: ...*you need to know all the things...*, causal modeling implied causative: ...*because...*

(45)

(45)

And if you can *look* at fear in relationship to me—

Sentence fragment. Causal modeling conjunction: *And...*, *...if...*, embedded command: *...can look at fear...*, presuppositions: *...can look at...*, *...in relationship to ...*, selectional restriction: *...look...fear*, nominalization: *fear...*, *relationship...*

(46)

(46)

and there was no reason to be afraid of me—

Conjunction: *...and ...*, presupposition: *...no reason to be afraid...*, nominalization: *...reason...*, deletion: *...for whom to be afraid?*

(47)

(47)

but you did have a sense of fear.

Causal modeling conjunction: *...but...*, presupposition: *...had a sense of fear...*, missing referential index: *...sense of fear...*, nominalization: *...sense...*, *fear...*, unspecified verbs: *...had ...*

(48)

(48)

Now you can look at that fear and *wonder* just exactly what caused it in various ways.

Presuppositions: *...can look at that fear...*, *wonder...just exactly...*, *... caused it...*, unspecified verbs: *...look...*, *wonder ...*, *...caused...*, missing referential index: *...that fear...*, *it...*, *...various ways...*, embedded command: *...wonder just exactly...*, nominalization: *...fear...*, *ways...*

(49)

(49)

Now, it may be getting warm in here.

Presupposition: *...getting warm...*, *in here...*,

unspecified verb: ...*getting*..., missing referential index: ...*it*..., deletion: *warm for whom?*

(49-60)

both clients attend to (R-operator) K variable of ongoing 4-tuple; meta-instructions to hold constant K variable of present 4-tuple while transderivationally searching (L-operators are V and A) for other 4-tuples both positive and negative.

(50)

I think both you and Monde would enjoy having it cool and comfortable.

(50)

Presupposition: *both you...would enjoy... having...cool...comfortable...*, unspecified verbs: ...*think..., enjoy ..., missing referential index:* ...mind reading: ...*think both...enjoy...*

(51)

I think it's very nice.

(51)

Unspecified verb: ...*think...*, missing referential index: *it's*, presupposition: ...*very...*, deletion: ...*nice for whom?*

(52)

because you here, sleeping soundly in bed, you enjoy a swim in the ocean or the lake, or the swimming pool.

(52)

Cause-effect: ...*because...*, presuppositions: ...*sleeping soundly..., ...enjoy a swim..., in the ocean..., in the lake..., ...in the swimming pool...*, unspecified verbs: *sleeping, enjoy,* missing referential index: ...*in bed..., a swim..., the ocean..., the lake..., the swimming pool...*, sentence fragment.

(53)

You can *meet* friends in your dreams, you can *hear* them talk and you can talk to them, you can drive a car, *take* an airplane ride, *hike* in the woods.

(53)

Presuppositions: ...*can meet friends...in your dreams...can hear them ...can talk to them...can drive a car..., ...take an airplane ride..., ..hike in the woods...*, embedded commands: ...*can meet friends..., can hear them*

..., ...*take*..., ...*hike*...,
unspecified verbs: ...
meet, take..., missing
referential index: ...
friends..., *in your
dreams*..., ...*them*..., ...
them..., ...*a car*..., *an
airplane ride*..., ...*the
woods*...

(54)

But all the time this is going on, you're still lying in bed.

(54)

Implied causative: ...*but*
..., presuppositions: ...
this is going on..., ...
still lying in bed..., unspecified verb: ...*going
lying*..., missing referential index: ...*all the time*
..., ...*this*..., *in bed*...,
nominalization: *time*.

(55)

You're not moving, not talking.

(55)

Presuppositions: ...*not
moving*..., *not talking*,
deletion: ...*not moving
what/how?* ...*not talk-
ing to whom about
what?*, unspecified
verbs: ...*talking* ...., ...,
moving...

(56)

Your unconscious has stored away many stores and many understandings, and your dreams are dreams in which you *review* your experience;

(56)

Presuppositions: *uncon-
scious has stored away*...
...*dreams are dreams*...,
...*in which you review*
..., embedded com-
mand: ...*review your
experience*..., missing referential index: ...*many
memories*..., *many un-
derstandings*..., ...
dreams..., *dreams*...,
your experience..., un-
specified verbs: *stored,
review*, nominalizations:
*unconscious, memories,
understandings, dreams,*

experience, deletions: *memories of what/ whom?, understandings of what/whom? dreams of what?, experience of what/whom?...*

(57)

(57)

and in the dreams you also *put together* ideas for better understandings...

Causal modeling conjunction: *...and...*, presupposition: *...in the dreams you...put together...*, embedded command: *...put together ideas and...*, unspecified verb: *put together*, nominalizations: *dreams, ideas, understandings,* deletions: *dreams of what/whom?, ideas of what?, understandings of what?*, referential index: *...the dreams..., ideas..., ...better understandings...*

(58)

(58)

You dream you're in a snowstorm and *be* very cold, and the truth is you're warmly in bed.

Presuppositions: *...you dream..., ...you're warmly...*, embedded command: *...and be very cold...*, causal modeling conjunction: *...and..., ...and...*, unspecified verb: *...dream ...*, missing referential index: *...a snow storm ..., the truth...in bed...*, nominalization: *...truth*, sentence fragment.

(59)

(59)

You can *dream* that you're very hungry, yet you ate a good dinner.

Presupposition: *...can dream..., ...very hungry ..., ...you are..., a good dinner...*, unspecified verb: *dream*, embedded command: *you can dream...*, missing referential index: *...a good dinner...*, implied causative: *...yet...*

(60)

(60)

Anything that happens to you can *come forth* as a dream, and you never have to *be worried* about it.

Presuppositions: *...can come forth..., as a dream..., ...never have to be worried...*, embedded command: *...can come forth..., ...never have to be worried...*, unspecified verbs: *... happens..., come forth ..., ...worried...*, missing referential index: *Anything..., ...a dream..., ...about it...*

(61)

(61)

(61-63)

Because your unconscious is sorting over your memories, your understandings, your hopes, your anticipation, your wishes—

Causal modeling cause-effect: *...because...*, presuppositions: *...unconscious is sorting...*, unspecified verb: *sorting,* nominalizations: *unconscious, memories, understandings, hopes, anticipations, wishes,* missing referential index: *...your memories..., ... your understandings..., ...your hopes..., your anticipation...your wishes.*

meta-instructions to re-organize previous 4-tuples.

(62)

(62)

and trying to *make* for a new arrangement of everything that you have learned—

Causal modeling conjunction: *...and...*, presuppositions: *...trying to make..., that you have learned...*, unspecified verb: *...make, learned,* embedded command: *... make for a new arrangement...*, missing referential index: ... *a new arrangement...*, *...of everything...*, nominalization: *...arrangement...*

(63)

(63)

a new arrangement that will be for your betterment and for your satisfaction.

Presuppositions: *...that will be for your betterment...*, *for your satisfaction...*, unspecified verb: *...be...*, missing referential index: *...a new arrangement...*, nominalizations: *arrangement...*, *betterment...*, *satisfaction...*

(64)

(64)

(64)

And it's very nice to be comfortable, comfortably cool, at ease.

Causal modeling conjunction: *...and...*, presuppositions: *...very nice to be comfortably ...*, *comfortably cool...*, *at ease...*, unspecified verb: *be*, nominalizations: *ease*, missing referential index: *its...*

attend to (R-operator) K variable of present 4-tuple.

(65)

(65)

(65-68)

And as you are that way, you *review* your understandings of values of life.

Causal modeling implied causative: *...and as...*, presuppositions: *...are that way...*, *review your understandings...*, missing referential index: *...that way...*, *your understandings...*, nominalizations: *...way...*, *understandings...*, *.. values...*, *life...*, unspecified verb: *...review...*, embedded command: *...review your understandings...*

meta-instructions to reorganize previous 4-tuple (L-operator is V)

(66)

(66)

You reach an under-

Presuppositions: *...such*

standing that every happiness is earned and, if given to you, it's merited.

an understanding..., happiness is earned... if given...it's merited..., unspecified verbs: ...reach..., earned..., merited..., nominalization: ...understanding ..., happiness..., missing referential index: *...an understanding..., ... every happiness..., ...it* deletion: *understanding of what?, given by whom?*

(67)

(67)

Because there is no such thing as a free gift; you have to *earn* it or have to *merit* it.

Causal modeling cause-effect: *...because...,* presuppositions: *...no such thing as a free gift..., have to earn..., have to merit...,* unspecified verbs: *...earn..., ...merit ...,* embedded command: *...have to earn..., have to merit...,* missing referential index: *...such thing..., a free gift..., it..., it...*

(68)

(68)

And merit requires labor and effort on your part.

Causal conjunction: ... *and...,* presupposition: *...merit requires labor..., effort..., on your part...,* unspecified verb: *...requires...,* nominalizations· *...merit ..., ...labor..., ...effort.*

(69)

(69)

(69-73)

And what do you need to fear?

Causal modeling conjunction: *...and...,* unspecified verb: *...need,* nominalization: *...fear...* deletion: *...fear of?*

Metaphor.

(70)

(70)

Very little that you need to fear.

Presupposition: ...*very little...*, *you need to fear...*, unspecified verb: *need...*, nominalization: *fear...*, missing referential index: ...*very little...* deletion: ...*fear of?*

(71)

(71)

I know that all my life I have encountered people who were afraid that they would starve to death.

Presupposition: ...*who were afraid...*, *they would starve...to death* ..., unspecified verbs: *encountered, afraid,* ...*starve...*, missing referential index: ...*people* ..., ...*they...*, nominalizations: ...*death...*

(72)

(72)

But in all the time I've been in medical practice, I have never seen a person who starved to death.

Causal modeling implied causative: ...*But...*, missing referential index: ... *all the time...*, ...*a person...*, nominalizations: ...*medical practice...*, ... *death...*, unspecified verbs: ...*been...*

(73)

(73)

It takes a great deal of effort to *do that.*

Presupposition: ...*takes a great deal of effort...*, unspecified verb: *takes,* missing referential index: ...*it...*, ...*that...*, ...*a great deal of effort...*, nominalizations: ...*deal* ..., *effort...*, embedded command...*do that...*

(74)

(74)

(74-82)

Enough in the way of bad luck can occur, so that you don't need to *add* to it yourself.

Presuppositions: ...*E-nough...can occur...*, ...*don't need to add...*, unspecified verbs: *occur, add,* nominalizations: ...

meta-instructions for re-organization of previous negative K 4-tuples; suggestions for amnesia.

bad luck..., way..., embedded command: ... don't need to add...

(75)

(75)

You'll always have a full supply of that, but you always need to *add* to the good luck that you *achieve*.

Presuppositions: ...*always a full supply...*, ... *always need to add...*, ...*to the good luck...*, ...*you achieve...*, embedded command: ... *add to the good luck...*, ...*that you achieve...*, unspecified verbs: *have, add, achieve,* nominalizations: ...*supply...*, ... *luck...*

(76)

(76)

And you'll *achieve* it on your own merit.

Causal modeling conjunction: ...*and...*, presupposition: ...*you'll achieve it...*, *on your... own merit...*, unspecified verb: ...*achieve...*, missing referential index: ...*it...*, nominalization: *merit,* embedded command: ...*you'll achieve.*

(77)

(77)

and that way you will really *enjoy* everything.

Causal modeling conjunction: ...*and...*, presupposition: ...*really enjoy everything...*, unspecified verb: *enjoy,* missing referential index: ...*that way...*, ...*everything...*, embedded command: ...*really enjoy...*

(78)

(78)

Now I do not need to talk all the time.

Deletion: ...*talk about what/whom...*, ...*talk to whom?...*, missing referential index: ...*all the*

time..., nominalization:
...time...

(79)

(79)

It's important for you
to realize that your
unconscious mind
can *start* a train of
thought,

Presuppositions: *...It's
important...*, *...to realize...*, *...mind can start
...*, unspecified verbs:
...realize..., *...start...*,
missing referential index:
its, *...a train of thought
...*, nominalization: *unconscious mind, thought
...*, embedded com-
mand: *unconscious can
start...*

(80)

(80)

and *develop* it without
your conscious know-
ledge—

Causal modeling con-
junction: *...and...*, presuppositions: *...develops
it...*, *...without your
conscious knowledge...*,
unspecified verb: *...de-
velop...*, embedded com-
mand: *...and develop it
...*, missing referential
index: *...it...*, nominalization: *...conscious
knowledge...*

(81)

(81)

and *reach* conclu-
sions, and let your
conscious mind be-
come aware of those
conclusions...

Causal modeling con-
junction: *...and...*, *...
and...*, presuppositions:
...reach conclusions...,
...become aware..., un-
specified verbs: *...reach
...*, *...aware...*, missing
referential index: *...con-
clusions...*, *those conclusions...*, nominaliza-
tions: *...conscious mind,
conclusions...*, embed-
ded command: *...reach
conclusions...*

(82)

(82)

And you can *enjoy* discovering so many things that are possible for you.

Causal modeling conjunction: ...*and*..., presuppositions: ...*can enjoy discovering*..., ...*things that are possible* ..., embedded command: ...*can enjoy discovering*..., unspecified verbs: ...*enjoy*..., *discovering*..., *possible*..., missing referential index: ...*so many things*...

(83)

(83)

(83-94)

When I see patients, I really want them to *do* a great deal of thinking,

Causal modeling, implied causative: ...*when*..., missing referential index: ...*patients*..., ...*them*..., ...*a great deal*..., presuppositions: ...*do a great deal of*..., embedded command: ...*do a great deal of thinging*, unspecified verb: ...*thinking*...

Metaphor.

(84)

(84)

because I don't know what's right for them.

Causal modeling, cause-effect: ...*because*..., missing referential index: ... *what's right*..., ...*for them*..., unspecified verb: ...*know*...

(85)

(85)

They have to *reach* that through an understanding of what they know, have experienced.

Missing referential index: ...*they*..., ...*that*..., ...*an understanding*..., ...*they*..., presupposition: ...*have to reach*..., ...*through an understanding*..., ...*they know*..., ...*have experienced*..., unspecified verbs: *...reach..., ... know..., ...experienced ...,* embedded command: *...have to reach that...,* nominalization: *...understanding...*

(86)

(86)

And each person can *put* past experiences and learnings together in a way that is satisfying...

Causal modeling conjunction: *...and...,* presupposition: *...person can put..., ...together in a way...,* unspecified verbs: *...put..., ...together...,* deletions: *... satisfying for whom?,* nominalizations: *...experiences, learnings, way,* missing referential index: *...each person..., past experiences..., learnings..., ...in a way ...,* embedded command: *...put past experiences and learnings together...*

(87)

(87)

Now you're sitting here in comfort and ease,

Presupposition: *...in comfort and ease...,* nominalization: *...comfort..., ease...,* mind reading: *...you're sitting ..., comfort...*

(88)

(88)

and you're learning about yourself without knowing just how you're learning.

Causal modeling conjunction: *...and...,* presuppositions: *...learning about yourself..., without knowing just how...,* unspecified verb: *learning, knowing, learning...* deletion: *...learning what?*

(89)

In our present day culture, there's much talk about meditation

(89)

Nominalizations: ...*culture...*, ...*meditations...*, ...*talk...*, deletions: ... *much talk by whom...*, ...*about what?...*

(90)

which only means that we all ought to do a bit of thinking, a bit of understanding.

(90)

Presuppositions: ...*all ought to do...*, unspecified verbs: *do...*, *thinking ..., understanding...*, referential index: ...*we ..., ...a bit of..., ...a bit of...*

(91)

And we need not *do it* in some rigid way:

(91)

Causal modeling conjunction: ...*and...*, presuppositions: ...*need not do..., ...in some rigid way...*, missing referential index: ...*we..., it..., some rigid way...*, unspecified verbs: *do*, nominalizations: ...*way ...*, embedded command: ...*do it...*

(92)

we can *take* our dreams, we can *take* spare moments.

(92)

Presuppositions: ...*can take our dreams..., ... can take spare moments ...*, unspecified verbs: ...*take...take...*, deletions: *dreams of what/ whom?, moments when? ...*, nominalizations: *dreams, moments*, missing referential index: ...*we...we...*, embedded command: ...*take our dreams...take spare moments...*

(93)

(93)

We do not need to make a show of meditation.

Causal modeling conjunction: *...but...*, presuppositions; *thinking for the self...by the self ...freely...easily...*, nominalizations: *mediation ..., self...self...*, unspecified verbs: *...thinking..., ...thinking...*

...thinking..., deletions: *...thinking freely about what/whom? thinking easily about what/ whom?...*, missing referential index: *...for the self..., by the self.*

(94)

(94)

But meditation is thinking for the self, by the self, and thinking freely and easily, just wondering about what the self has to offer for the self.

Unspecified verbs: *... wondering..., ...offering ...,* nominalizations: *... self..., ...self...,* missing referential index: *...what the self..., for the self...*

(95)

(95)

(95-96)

Now comfort in a hot room is possible, yet you can *let* only cool thoughts come your way.

Presuppositions: *...comfort...is possible ..., ... can let only cool thoughts come...,* unspecified verbs: *...possible..., ...let..., ...come ...,* nominalization: *comfort, thoughts, way.* missing referential index: *...a hat room..., ...cool thoughts...,* embedded command: *...let only cool...,* implied causative: *...yet...,* selectional restriction, deletion: *hot for whom?/cool to whom?...*

links metaphor (83-94) to present 4-tuple.

(96)   (96)

You can *let* quiet thoughts come to you. You can let painless thoughts come to you.

Presuppositions: *...can let quiet thoughts come in..., ...let painless thoughts come...,* embedded command: *...let quiet thoughts come...,* unspecified verbs: *...let ...let...,* nominalizations: *...thoughts..., ...thoughts...,* deletions: *...quiet for whom?/ painless for whom?...,* selectional restrictions.

(97)   (97)   (97-114)

Now I'll tell you something that both of you can understand.

Presupposition: *...both of you can understand...* unspecified verb: *...understand...,* missing referential index: *...something...*

metaphor with direct quotes.

(98)   (98)

A patient was brought to my office by ambulance.

Missing referential index: *...a patient...,* deletion: *...brought when: by whom? for what?*

(99)   (99)

The patient had, possibly, three months more to live.

Missing referential index: *...the patient...,* deletion: *...live/how?...*

(100)   (100)

And the patient was in very great pain, and drugs didn't seem to help at all.

Presuppositions: *...very great pain...,* unspecified verbs: *...help...,* missing referential index: *...the patient..., very great pain..., ...drugs...,* nominalization: *...pain...*

(101)

And she hadn't had drugs for more than eight hours when she arrived at my office.

(101)

Causal modeling conjunction: ...*and*..., missing referential index: ... *she*..., ...*drugs*..., unspecified verb:...*arrived*.

(102)

And she was wheeled in, and she said,

(102)

Causal modeling, conjunction: ...*and*..., missing referential index: ... *she*..., ...*she*..., deletion: ...*wheeled by whom/to here?*...*said to whom?*

(103)

"My doctor said you would *use* hypnosis to control my pain.

(103)

Quotes: Embedded command: *use hypnosis to* ..., unspecified verb: ... *control*..., nominalization: ...*pain*.

(104)

And I think that's ridiculous.

(104)

Continued quotes: causal conjunction: ...*and*..., unspecified verb: ... *think*..., referential index: ...*that's*..., deletion: *ridiculous to whom?*

(105)

Even drugs don't *control* my pain.

(105)

Continued quotes: embedded command: ... *control my pain*..., referential index: ...*drugs* ..., unspecified verb: ... *control*..., nominalization: ...*pain*...

(106)

And in just a spoken word—that sounds ridiculous."

(106)

Continued quotes: ... *causal conjunction*: ...

and..., missing referential index: *...a spoken word..., ...that...,* deletion: *...ridiculous to whom?*

(107)

(107)

I said, "Madam, just listen to me, and see if you can *understand* what I mean.

Quotes: Embedded command: *...can understand:* ...unspecified verb: *...understand...,* deletion: *...listen to me say waht?* ...missing referential index: *...what I mean...*

(108)

(108)

As you sit there, if you saw a very hungry looking tiger walk through that door into this room, and look at you and lick its chops, how much pain do you suppose you would feel?"

Quotes: causal modeling conjunction: *...and ...if...,* missing referential index: *...you..., ...there..., ...a hungry looking tiger..., ...that door..., ...this room..., ...you..., ...how much pain..., ...you...,* nominalization: *hungry, pain.*

(109)

(109)

She said, "I wouldn't feel any pain, I'd be thinking about the tiger. And now I notice I don't have any pain now, because I've gotten a new view of things."

Quotes: referential index: *...she...,* deletion: *said to whom/when?* ...missing referential index: *...the tiger..., ...things ...,* implied causal conjunction: *...and..., ...because...,* unspecified verbs: *...thinking..., ...notice..., ...have..., ...gotten...,* nominalization: *...pain..., ...pain ..., ...view...*

(110)

(110)

And when she left, I asked her what she was going to do.

Conjunction: *...and..., ...when...,* unspecified

verb: *...left going...,* missing referential index: *...her...,* *...what...,* *...she...,* deletion: *...do about what for whom?*

(111)

And she said, "I'm going to *have* a good time, but I don't think the nurses will *understand* about the tiger that I'm going to *keep* under my bed.

(111)

Conjunction: *...and...,* *...but...,* referential index: *...she...,* quotes, embedded commands: *...have...,* *...a good time ...,* *...understand...,* *...keep...,* missing referential index: *...a good time ...,* *...the nurses...,* *...that tiger...,* unspecified verbs: *...have...,* *...t think...,* *...understand.*

(112)

I don't think the doctor will *understand* either."

(112)

Quotes, embedded command: *...understand...,* missing referential index: *...the doctors...,* unspecified verb: *...think ...,* *...understand...,* deletion: *...understand what?...*

(113)

And everytime they asked her if she wanted drugs for her pain, she said,

(113)

Conjunction: *...and...,* missing referential index: *...everytime...,* *...they ...,* *...her...,* *...she...,* *...she...,* unspecified verbs: *...wanted...,* nominalization: *...pain, drugs...*

(114)

"No, I'm keeping the tiger there, anytime I need him."

(114)

Quotes: missing referential index: *...the tiger ...,* *...there...,* *...anytime...,* unspecified verb: *...keeping...,* *...need...*

(115)

Well, you've got a lot of things to help you, and *keep* them handy —handy in every possibly way.

(115)

Presuppositon: *...got a lot...*, *...keep them handy...*, unspecified verbs: *...got...*, *...keep ...*, missing referential index: *...things...*, *them ...*, *every possible way ...*, deletions: *...handy how?...*, causal modeling conjunction: *...and ...*, nominaliation: *... way...*, embedded command: *...keep them handy...*

(115-116)

meta-instructions for utilization of past 4-tuples; organ language for arm levitation.

(116)

And know that your own brain cell responses can *meet* your needs.

(116)

Causal modeling implied causative: *...and...*, unspecified verbs: *... know...*, *...meet...*, nominalizations: *...responses...*, *...needs...*, selectional restriction, missing referential index: *...onw brain cell, your needs...*

(117)

Now you had difficulty while Monde was in a trance in breathing.

(117)

Presupposition: *...mind knows...*, *...lot of things ...*, unspecified verb: *... knows...*, nominalizations: *...unconscious mind...*, missing referential index: *...a lot...*, *... things...*, deletion: *... know a lot of what/ whom?*

(117-126)

links utilization of past 4-tuples to client's (Nick) present 4-tuple (breathing).

(118)

You breathed very loudly.

(118)

Deletions: *loudly to whom/compared to what? whom?* presupposition: *very loudly.*

(119)

(119)

You're breathing very nicely, very comfortably, right now.

Presuppositions: ... *breathing very nicely..., comfortably..., ...right now...,* deletions: ... *nicely to whom? ...comfortably for whom?*

(120)

(120)

And why shouldn't you. You know how.

Implied causative: *...and ..., * deletions: *...why shouldn't you what? ...know how to do what/when?..., * presupposition: *...you know how ..., * unspecified verb: ... *know...*

(121)

(121)

And I feel very pleased that you did not need to think you had to breathe that loudly as you did before.

Implied causative: *...and ..., ...that..., * deletion: *...feel very pleased..., about..., * presuppositions: *...you did not need..., ...that loudly..., * unspecified verbs: ... *..., ...that loudly..., * unspecified verbs: *...need ..., ...think..., * nominalization: *...pleased, * missing referential index: ... *that loudly..., * deletion: *...before what/when?*

(122)

(122)

And you can be pleased.

Causal modeling implied causative: *...and..., * presupposition: *...can be pleased, * unspecified verb: *...pleased...*

(123)

(123)

Your unconscious

Presuppositions: *...mind*

mind knows a lot of things.

knows..., ...lot of things ..., unspecified verb: ... knows..., nominalizations: ...unconscious mind..., missing referential index: ...a lot..., ... things..., deletion: ... know a lot of what/ whom?

(124)

(124)

And I rather think that loud breathng, on your part, was a setting-up of something you could *notice*—

Causal modeling, conjunction: ...and..., presuppositions: ...was a setting up..., ...could notice..., unspecified verbs: ...think..., ...notice..., missing referential index: ...that loud breathing..., ...a setting up of something..., deletion: ...loud to whom? ..., ...on your part of what/how?..., mind reading: embedded command: ...something you could notice...

(125)

(125)

something that you could *notice*, as abscence, when I worked with you directly...

Presuppositions: ... something..., ...you could notice..., as abscence..., unspecified verbs: ...notice..., ... worked..., referential index: ...something..., causal modeling implied causative: ...when..., deletions: ...directly..., embedded command: ... something you could notice..., sentence fragment.

(126)

(126)

And you had a slight smile on your face

Causal modeling conjunction: ...And..., ...

when I mentioned that.	*when...,* referential index: *...a slight smile...,* *...that...*	

(127)	(127)	(127-130)
It's nice to know that we know more than we know about.	Presuppositions: *...nice to know..., ...that we know..., ...more than we know...,* unspecified verbs: *...know..., ...know..., ...know...,* missing referential index: *...it's..., ...we..., ...we ...,* nominalization: *...nice...,* deletions: *...nice to whom?..., ...that we know more than what/ about what/whom?...*	digital confusion; meta-instructions to attend to (R-operator) K variable of positive K 4-tuples.

(128)	(128)
And we can *understand* more than we think we *can.*	Causal modeling conjunction: *...and...,* presupposition: *...we can understand..., more than..., we think...we can...,* unspecified verbs: *...understand..., ...think...,* missing referential index: *...we..., we..., we...,* deletions: *more than what? we can do what to whom? ...* embedded command: *... we can understand...*

(129)	(129)
And we can *feel pleasure* at times when we think we can't.	Presuppositions: *...feel pleasure..., ...at times ...,* unspecified verbs: *...feel..., think...,* missing referential index: *... we...at times..., we..., we...,* nominalizations: *...pleasure...,* embedded command: *...feel pleasure...*

(130)

(130)

And we should be *willing to feel*, fully the pleasures and the happiness that we want, cause all our feelings are done by ourselves.

Causal modeling conjunction: *...and..., ...'cause..., ...and...,* presupposition: *...be willing to feel fully..., ...feelings are done by ourselves...,* unspecified verbs: *...willing..., ...feel..., ...want..., ...done...,* missing referential index: *...we..., ...the pleasures..., ...the happiness..., ...our feelings..., ...by ourselves...,* nominalizations: *...pleasures..., ...happiness..., ...feelings ...,* embedded command: *...be willing to feel...*

(131)

(131)

(131-139)

We can use other people as stimuli.

Presupposition: *...can use other people..., as stimuli...,* referential index: *...we..., ...other people..., ...as stimuli ...,* deletion: *...stimuli for what?...,* unspecified verb: *...use...,* nominalization: *...stimuli...*

metaphor; meta-instructions to utilize past 4-tuples anchored to Arizona.

(132)

(132)

You meet an excellent teacher, and he can teach you a lot of new ideas.

Presuppositions: *...meet an excellent teacher..., ...he can teach you..., ...a lot of new ideas...,* unspecified verbs: *...meet..., ...teach...,* missing referential index: *...an excellent teacher..., ...he..., ...a lot..., ...new ideas...,* nominalization: *...ideas...,* deletion: *...a lot compared to what?*

(133)

—*be stimulated* into accumulating his own wealth of ideas.

(133)

Embedded command: ... *be stimulated...*, presuppositions: ...*into accumulating...*, ...*own wealth of ideas...*, unspecified verbs: ...*stimulated...*, ...*accumulating...*, missing referential ...*his...*, *wealth of ideas* ..., nominalization: ... *ideas...*, ...*wealth...*

(134)

You learned something about Arizona today; you're learning a lot more about yourself.

(134)

Presuppositions: ...*you learned something...*, ... *about Arizona...*, *today* ..., *you're learning a lot more...*, *about yourself* ..., unspecified verbs: ... *learned...learning...*, missing referential index: ...*something about Arizona...*, ...*a lot more...*

(135)

And as long as you *remember Arizona*, you're going to *remember* some of your learnings—a lot of the learnings.

(135)

Causal modeling implied causative: ...*and as long as...*, presuppositions: ...*as long as you remember Arizona...*, ... *going to remember some...*, ...*learnings...*, ...*a lot of...*, embedded command: ...*remember Arizona...*, unspecified verbs: ...*remember...*, ...*remember some of your learning...*, ...*remember...*, missing referential index: ...*some of your learnings*, ...*a lot...*, nominalization: ...*learnings, learnings,*

(136)

Because you've learn-

(136)

Causal modeling, cause-ed them in Arizona, and you'll never be able to forget Arizona.

effect: ...*because*..., presuppositions: ...*you've learned them...in Arizona..., never be able to forget Arizona...,* unspecified verbs: ...*learned..., forget...,* missing referential index: ...*them ...*

---

(137)

And so your new understandings, new learnings, are *tied— tied down, tied in—* because they are a part of a greater learning.

(137)

Causal modeling cause-effect: ...*and so because...,* presuppositions: ...*are tied...tied down...tied in...,* unspecified verbs: ...*tied ..., tied down...tied in ...,* missing referential index: ...*new understandings...new learnings...they..., a greater learning...,* nominalizations: ...*understandings ..., learnings..., learning...,* selectional restriction, embedded command: ...*tied..., ...tied ..., ...tied...*

---

(138)

And the same is true of you, Monde.

(138)

Causal modeling conjunction: ...*and...,* presupposition: ...*same is true...,* deletion: ...*the same is true/how?*

---

(139)

You learn a great deal; it's always going to be a part of you; and you want every good new learnings to be a part of you.

(139)

Presuppositions: ...*learn a great deal...always going to be a part...want every...to be a part...,* unspecified verb: *learn ...going...want...be...,* missing referential index; ...*a great deal...its...a part...every good new*

learning...a part....
nominalization, *learning*
...part..., deletions: *...a*
great deal compared to
what? [a part how?]

(140)

(140)

(140-144)

Some way or other, your unconscious mind knew that you would go into a trance while I put Monde in.

Presuppositions: *...some way or another...mind knew that...would go into a trance while...*, unspecified verbs: *... knew...go...put...*, missing referential index: *some way...or another ...*, causal modeling implied causative: *...while ...*, nominalizations: *... unconscious mind...*, *...trance...*, deletions: *... put in where/how?...*

disassociation for conscious/unconscious mind; transderivational search to previous trance 4-tuple; arm levitation suggestions.

(141)

(141)

How did your unconscious mind know, in advance, how to *direct* your attention only to your hand?

Presupposition: *...mind know...in advance...direct your attention...only to your hand...*, unspecified verbs: *...know ..., direct...*, deletion: *in advance of what? ...* nominalizations: *...unconscious mind...attention...*, embedded command: *...direct your attention only to your hand...*

(142)

(142)

But it did.

Causal modeling: *...but ...*, missing referential index: *...it...*, deletion: *...it did what? when? to whom?...*

(143)

(143)

And in that way, you

Causal modeling con-

became unaware of a lot of things your unconscious wanted to *learn*.

junction: ...*and*..., presuppositions: ...*in that way*..., ...*became unaware*..., ...*unconscious wanted to learn*..., unspecified verbs: ...*unaware*..., ...*wanted*..., ...*learn*..., missing referential index: ...*in that way*..., ...*a lot*..., ...*of things*..., nominalizations: ...*way*..., ...*unconscious mind*..., embedded command: ...*learn*...

(144)

(144)

And it took over, and did learn.

Causal modeling conjunction: ...*and*..., presuppositions: ...*it took over*..., ...*did learn*..., unspecified verb: ...*took*..., *learn*..., missing referential index: ...*it*...

(145)

(145)

(145-150)

Now I want both of you to *be aware* of the tremendous importance of comfort and ease:

Embedded command: ...*be aware of the*..., presuppositions: ...*to be aware*..., unspecified verbs: ...*want*...*aware*... nominalization: ...*comfort*..., ...*ease*..., missing referential index: ...*the tremendous importance*..., deletion: ...*important to whom?*

both clients instructed to attend to (R-operator) K variable of positive K 4-tuples; meta-instructions to utilize past 4-tuples; organ language used to suggest arm levitation.

(146)

(146)

a sense of security; a sense of readiness;

Sentence fragment, nominalizations: ...*sense*..., *sense*..., deletions: ...*security for whom? readiness for what?*...

(147)

(147)

a full knowledge that

Presuppositions: ...*you*

come what may, you can *meet* it and *handle* it—and *enjoy* doing it.

can meet...handle...enjoy doing..., embedded commands: *...can meet it and handle it...enjoy doing it...*, unspecified verbs: *...come..., ...meet..., ...handle..., ...enjoy...*, missing referential index: *...come what may..., it..., it..., it...*, deletion: *...a full knowledge of what?...*

(148)

(148)

It's also a nice learning to *come up* against the situation that you can't handle —and then later *think* it over, and *realize* that, too, was a learning that's useful in many, many different ways.

Missing referential index: *...a nice learning ..., the situation..., it..., that..., a learning...in many..., many different ways...*, embedded command: *...come up against..., ...think..., ...realize...*, presuppositions: *...later think it over...and realize...*, deletion: *...nice for whom? useful to whom/how? ...*, unspecified verbs: *...come up..., handle..., think..., realize...*, nominalizations: *...learning ..., situation..., learning ..., ways...*

(149)

(149)

It allows you to *assess* your strength.

Presuppositions: *...allows you to assess...*, missing referential index: *...it...*, unspecified verbs: *...allows, assess,* nominalization:*... strength...*, embedded command: *...assess your strength...*

(150)

(150)

It also allows you to *discover* the areas in which you need to

Presuppositions: *...also allows you to discover... which you need to use*

use more of your own security, which rests within yourself.

..., *your own security...,* ...*which rests within yourself...,* unspecified verbs: ...*allows...discover...need...,* nominalizations: ...*areas ...,* ...*security..,* embedded command: ...*discover the areas...,* missing referential index: ...*it...,* *the areas...*

(151)   (151)   (151-159)

And remember always that you're unique.

Causal modeling conjunction: ...*and...,* presupposition: ...*remember always...,* unspecified verb: ...*remember...,* deletion: ...*unique in what way?*

metaphor with direct quotes.

(152)   (152)

And all that you have to do is let people *see* that you are you.

Causal modeling conjunction: ...*and...,* presupposition: ...*all that you have to do...,* missing referential index: ... *all people...,* embedded command:..*see that you ...,* unspecified verb: ... *do...*

(153)   (153)

One of the things I learned very early— was that at a house call to *see* a little child, beautifully dressed, hair combed

Missing referential index: ...*one of the things ...,* ...*very early...,* *a house call...a little child ...,* unspecified verb: ... *learned...,* embedded command: ...*see...,* deletion: ...*beautifully dressed to whom?...*

(154)   (154)

—and the face of the child would say, "Nobody likes me, just nobody."

Causal modeling conjunction: ...*and...,* mind reading, missing referential index: ...*the child*

..., ...*nobody*..., ...*just nobody*..., unspecified verb: ...*likes*...

(155)

(155)

And the child was right.

Causal modeling conjunction: ...*and*..., missing referential index: ...*the child*..., deletions: *right about what: Presupposition:* ...was right ..., nominalization: ... *right*...

(156)

(156)

Go to another home to see a little child, dirty face, untidy, hair tangled, and the child gives a gurgle of glee and rushes toward you—

Missing referential index: ...*another home*..., ...*a little child*..., ...*the child*..., deletions: ... *dirty to whom?*..., ...*untidy to whom?* ..., nominalizations: ...*glee*, unspecified verb: ...*gives* ..., ...*rushes*...

(157)

(157)

and the face says, "everybody likes me."

Causal modeling conjunction; ...*and*..., missing referential index: ... *the face*..., quotes, referential index: ...*everybody*..., unspecified verb: ...*says*...

(158)

(158)

And that child is right, everybody does ...

Causal modeling: ...*and* ..., presupposition: ... *child is right*..., missing referential index: ...*that child*..., ...*everybody*..., nominalization: ...*right* ..., deletion: ..*right about what?*..., *everybody does what?*...

(159)

To *have* that attitude is a precious possession— and you're entitled to it.

(159)

Embedded command: ... *have that attitude...,* presupposition: ...*you're entitled...,* missing referential index: ...*that attitude..., ...a previous possession...it..,* unspecified verbs: ...*have..., ...entitled...,* nominalizations: ...*attitude...*

(160)

As part of Arizona, and the total learning of Arizona, the Indian meets the rattlesnake and says, "You *go* your way, little brother and I will go mine."

(160)

Selectional restriction, causal modeling: ...*as...,* missing referential index: ...*the total learnings..., ...the indian..., ...the rattle snake...,* Quotes: referential index: ...*your way...,* embedded command: ...*go your way...*

(160-162)

metaphor with direct quotes.

(161)

And both the snake and the Indian are dignified and right.

(161)

Causal modeling conjunction: ...*and...,* presupposition: ...*dignified and right...,* missing referential index: ...*the snake..., the indian...,* nominalizations: ...*right* ...

(162)

And each goes his way in dignity, *in security,* in comfort, with respect.

(162)

Causal modeling conjunction: ...*and...,* missing referential index: ... *each..., ...his way...* unspecified verb: ...*goes* ...,* presuppositions: ... *in dignity..., ...in security..., ...in comfort..., with respect...,* nominalizations: ...*dignity..., ...security..., ...comfort*

..., ...*respect...*, phonological ambiguity: ...*insecurity...*

(163)

And I think self-
respect and the full
knowledge that you
have self-respect—

(163)

Sentence fragment, caus-
al modeling conjunction:
...*and...*, embedded
command: ...*have self
respect...*, unspecified
verb: ...*think...*, ...*have
...*, nominalizations: ...
self respect..., ...*knowledge...*, ...*self-respect
...*, referential index: ...*a
fully knowledge...*

(163-168)

transderivational search
for negative K 4-tuples
anchored to Arizona.

(164)

and you should have
that by virtue of being
alive, and willing to
do the things that
most interest you,
and to *do them well.*

(164)

Causal modeling con-
junction: ...*and...*, embedded commands: ...*do
the things...*, *do them
well,* presupposition: ...
well..., missing referential index: ...*that...*, ...
the thngs..., ...*them...*,
nominalizations: ...*vir-
tue...*, unspecified verbs:
...*have...*, ...*willing...*,
...*do...*, ...*interest...*, ...
do...

(165)

You both have uncer-
tainty in the past.

(165)

Presupposition: ..*both
have uncertainty...*, de-
letion: ...*uncertainty
about what?...*, unspeci-
fied verb: ...*have...*,
missing referential index:
...*in the past...*, nominalization: ...*uncer-
tainty...*

(166)

You can *leave* that
uncertainty.

(166)

Presupposition: ...*can
leave that...*, unspecified

verb: ...*leave*..., missing referential index: ...*that uncertainty*..., embedded command: ...*leave that*..., nominalization: ...*uncertainty*...

(167)

(167)

You can *leave it* in Arizona.

Presupposition: ...*leave it*..., unspecified verb: ...*leave*..., referential index: ...*it*..., embedded command: ...*leave it in* ...

(168)

(168)

It won't change Arizona; it'll change you.

Presupposition: ...*it'll change you*..., unspecified verb: ...*change*..., ... *change*..., missing referential index: ...*it*..., ...*it* ...

(169)

(169)

(169-177)

And the farmboy that I once was, back in Wisconsin—if I ever went back, I could take up those things, because they were good.

Causal modeling conjunction: ...*and*..., cause effect: ...*because*..., referential index: ...*those old things*..., ...*they*..., deletion: ...*good for whom?*...

metaphor; meta-instructions to use V variable as the lead (L-operator and R-operator are V) to negative K 4-tuples maintaining V/K disassociation.

(170)

(170)

And they are not a part of me anymore...

Causal modeling conjunction: ...*and*..., referential index: ...*they*..., *anymore*...

(171)

(171)

And the unpleasantnesses and unhappinesses of the past— *leave* them in the past, way back in the past.

Causal modeling conjunction: ...*and*..., missing referential index: ...*the unpleasantnesses, unhappinesses, ...of the past*..., ...*them*..., ...*in*

*the past..., ...way back
in the past...,* embedded
command: *...leave them
...,* unspecified verb: ...
leave..., nominaliza-
tions: *...unpleasantnes-
ses..., ...unhappinesses
...*

(172)

**And look forward to
the good days com-
ing, the new experi-
ences, the new under-
standings.**

(172)

Causal modeling: *...and
...,* presuppositions: ...
*look forward to..., ...
good days coming..., ...
new experiences..., ...
new understandings...,*
unspecified verbs: ...
look forward..., refer-
ential index:*...the good
days coming..., ...the
new experiences...,...the
understandings...,* nomi-
nalizations: *experiences
..., ...understandings...*

(173)

**And be aware that you
can *look* back at the
age of 40 to your lack
of understanding of
what happiness could
be at 40.**

(173)

Causal modeling con-
junction: *...and...,*
presupposition: *...that
you can look..., ...at the
age of 40..., ...your lack
of understanding...,* un-
specified verb: *...aware
..., ...look back..., ...
lack..., ...be...,* referential index: *...lack of
understanding...,* dele-
tion: *...happiness for
whom?...,* nominaliza-
tion: *...happiness...,* embedded command: ...
you can look back...

(174)

**Just as that time when
you were ten years
old, you could not
possibly *understand***

(174)

Causal modeling, impli-
ed causative: *...just as
...,* referential index: ...
that time when..., ...

what happiness of the 20's were, what the happiness of teen-age...	*happiness of the 20's..., ...happiness of teenage ...*, presuppositions: *... that time when you..., ...could not possibly understand..., ...happiness of 20's..., ...happiness of teenage...*, unspecified verbs: *...understand...*, embedded command: *...understand...*, nominalizations: *...happiness..., ...teenage...*, sentence fragment.

(175)

And the broken toys of your childhood—it really hurt to lose them, *see* them broken.	Causal modeling conjunction: *...and...*, referential index: *...the broken toys..., ...your childhood..., ...it...*, presupposition: *...it really hurt ...*, unspecified verb: *... hurt..., ...see...*, embedded command: *...see them broken...*

(176)

When we all *grow up*, having lost some things that we *forget about*—	Causal modeling, implied causative: *...when...*, referential index: *...we are..., ...something...*, embedded command: *... grow up..., forget about ...*, unspecified verbs: *...grow..., ...forget..., ...lost...*, presuppositions: *...lost some things ...., ...forget about...*, deletion: *...forget about what?*

(177)

and if we ever do remember them, we will *see* them differently than when it happened.	Causal modeling conjunction: *...and if...*, presuppositions: *...will see them differently than ...*, unspecified verb: *...*

remember..., ...happened..., deletion: ...differently for whom?..., missing referential index: ... them..., ...them..., ... when it..., embedded command: ...see them differently...

(178)   (178)   (178-183)

And that open window, Monde, had one meaning then, and such a pleasant meaning now: a totally different experience, a new learning.

Causal modeling conjunction: *...and..., ... and...,* presuppositions: *...had one meaning then ..., ...pleasant meaning now..., ...a different experience..., ...a new learning...,* ...referential index: *...that open window..., one meaning..., ...a pleasant meaning..., ...different experience..., ...a new learning...,* nominalization: *... meaning..., ...meaning..., ...experience..., ...learning...,* deletion: *...pleasant for whom?*

transderivational search (L-operator is V) to previous negative K 4-tuple (for Monde) maintaining anchored positive K (R-operator) variable.

(179)   (179)

That spanking when you broke the window—and now you can look back, see a spanking as something much different than when you received it.

Missing referential index: *...that spanking.., ...the window..., ...a spanking ..., ...something different...,* presupposition: *...can look back...see a spanking as somethng different...than whe...,* unspecified verbs: *... look back..., ...see..., ... received...,* causal modeling conjunction: *...and...*

(180)   (180)

And you can actually look back with pleasure, and *recall* how a spanking hurt, how

Causal modeling conjunction: *...and...,* presuppositions: *...can look back..., ...with pleasure* you felt tears.

..., ...*recall...*, ...*how a spanking hurt...*, ...*you felt tears...*, unspecified verbs: ...*look back...*, ... *recall...*, ...*felt...*, nominalization: ...*pleasure* ..., missing referential index: ...*a spanking...*, ...*tears...*, embedded command: ...*recall...*

(181)

(181)

Compared to the tears only proved that you were alive, with a good nervous system.

Deletion: ...*What compared to the tears?*, ... *good to whom?...*, presupposition: ...*tears only proved...*, unspecified verbs: ...*proved...*, *alive* ..., nominalization: ... *system...*, missing referential index: ...*the tears* ..., ...*a good nervous system...*

(182)

(182)

And it would have been terrible if you hadn't been able to feel that spanking— been terrible if you couldn't have cried.

Causal modeling conjunction: ...*and...*, deleltions: ...*terrible for whom/how?...terrible for whom/how?...*, presuppositions: ...*would have been terrible...*, ... *terrible...*, missing referential index: ...*it...*, ... *that spanking...*, unspecified verbs: ...*feel...*

(183)

(183)

In other words, reacting to the good and the bad, and dealing with it adequately— that's the real joy in life.

Missing referential index: ...*in other words...*, ...*the good...*, ...*the bad* ..., *it...*, ...*the real joy* ..., ...*in life...*, deletions: ...*real joy for whom/ when? ...adequately for whom?...*, nominalization: ...*good...*, ...*bad* ..., ...*joy...*, unspecified

verbs: ...*reacting...*, ...
dealing...

(184)

Now I want both of you, in your own thinking, in your own understanding, to continue to *look* at anything you wish, to *achieve* the understandings you're capable of achieving.

(184)

Presuppositions: ...*continue to look at anything ...*, ...*achieve...*, ...*your capable...*, unspecified verbs: ...*continue, look, wish, achieve, capable, achieving,* nominalizations: ...*thinking...*, *understandings...*, *understandings*, missing referential index: ...*anything ...*, embedded command: ...*look...*, ...*achieve...*

(184-186)

meta-instructions to generalize the V/K pattern set in 178-183.

(185)

Monde, you could look at the little girl chasing the ducks, and feeding the ducks breadcrumbs, the child splashing her feet in water — that beautiful sense of freedom — or you could *have* a beautiful sense of freedom, now.

(185)

Missing referential index: ...*the little girl...*, ...*the ducks...*, *the ducks ...*, ...*the child...*, nominalizations: ...*sense...*, ...*freedom...*, ...*sense...*, ...*freedom...*, deletion: ...*beautiful to whom?...* scope ambiguity: ...*now...*

(186)

Then you were able to *think* about a lot of things which you didn't need to.

(186)

Implied causative: ...*then...*, embedded command: ...*think...*, unspecified verb: ...*able...*, ...*think...*, ...*need...*, missing referential index: ...*a lot of things...*, nominalizations:...*things...*

(187)

And I know from my own experience, that

(187)

Causal modeling conjunction: ...*and...*, ...

(187-196)

anchors pattern set in 178-183 and generalize in 184-186 to Arizona.

it's wonderful to be able to be in a wheelchair—and I meet nice people...

and..., unsepcified verb: *...know...*, *...able...*, nominalizations: *...experience...*, deletion: *...wonderful for whom?* *...missing referential index: ...nice people...*

(188)

(188)

And I think life would be very, very bad if I could not have had the pleasure of meeting both of you—and I thank you.

Causal modeling conjunction: *...and...*, unspecified verb: *...think...*, nominalization: *...pleasure...*, *...life...*, deletions: *...bad for whom?*, *...thank for what?...*

(189)

(189)

You need to *keep* Arizona as a treasured part in all the learnings—as a treasured part of your life—

Embedded command: *... keep Arizona as a...*, presupposition: *...you need...*, unspecified verbs: *...need...*, *...keep ...*, missing referential index: *...all the learnings ...*, deletions: *...a treassured how for whom? ...*, nominalization: *... learning...*, treasure...

(190)

(190)

and to *use* those learnings to meet your wishes, your needs, your comfort.

Causal modeling conjunction: *... ... ...and...*, embedded command: *... use those learnings...*, unspecified verbs: *...use ...*, *...meet...*, nominalizations: *...learnings...*, *...wishes...*, *...needs...*, *...comfort...*, missing referential index: *... those learnings...*

(191)

And you are comfort-
able, are you not,
Monde? It's delightful
to be comfortable.

(191)

Conjunction: ...and...,
presupposition: ...are
comfortable..., tag ques-
tion: ...are you not...,
unspecified verb: ...
comfortable..., comfort-
able..., deletion: ...de-
lightful to whom?...

(192)

And you are comfort-
able, are you not,
Nick?
N: Yes.

(192)

Conjunction: ...and...,
presupposition:...are
comfortable..., tag ques-
tion: ...are you not?...,
unspecified verb: ...
comfortable...

(193)

E: Now would you
   ask a question of
   me?
N: No.

(193)

Referential index: ...a
question..., deletion: ...
question about what?...

(194)

E: Will you enjoy
   your thinking?
N: Yes.

(194)

Embedded command: ...
enjoy your thinking...,
unspecified verb: ...en-
joy..., deletion: ...think-
ing about what?...

(195)

E: And will you
   achieve better
   understandings?
N: Yes.

(195)

Causal modeling con-
junction: ...and..., em-
bedded command: ...
achieve better under-
standing..., deletion: ...
better than what? to
whom?..., nominaliza-
tion: ...understandings.

(196)

(196)

E: With less fear and more eagerness?
N: Yes.

Sentence fragment, nominalization: ...*fear* ..., ...*eagerness*..., deletions: ...*fear of what?* ... *more eagerness about?* ...presuppositions: ... *less fear, more eagerness* ...

(197)

(197)

(197-206)

E:It has been a pleasure to work with both of you.

Nominalization: ... *pleasure*..., ...*work*..., unspecified verb: ... *work*..., deletion: ... *pleasure for whom?*

re-orientation to present 4-tuple instructions.

(198)

(198)

And I want to thank both of you very much for working with me.

Causal modeling conjunction: ...*and*..., deletion: ...*working how?* ..., unspecified verb: ... *thank*..., presupposition: ...*very much*...

(199)

(199)

It's always a pleasure to do good work, and *do* good work with good materials.

Deletion: ...*pleasure for whom?*..., ...*good for whom/compared to what?*..., embedded command: ...*do good work*..., unspecified verbs: ...*good work*..., ...*good materials*..., nominalizaiton: ... *pleasure*..., ...*work*...

(200)

(200)

It's a pleasure.

Deletion: ...*pleasure for whom? how?*..., referential index: ...*its*..., nominalization: ...*pleasure*, presupposition: ...*rare*...

(201)

(201)

And now I'm tired, I think I'll let you both *awaken* at your own rate, in your own way.

Embedded command:... *awaken...,* presupposition: *...your own rate...,* *...your own way...,* nominalization: *...way ..., ...rate...,* unspecified verbs: *...think..., ... awaken...,* deletion: *... tired of what?*

(202)

(202)

Shut your eyes first, Monde, and then *awaken* at your own rate, in your own way.

Presuppositions: *...first ...,* causal modeling conjunction: *...and...*

(203)

(203)

You both had your eyes closed. So now, you can take your own time and wake up.

Tense change: *...had...,* deletion: *...eyes closed when?...,* implied causative: *...so now..., ...and ...,* presupposition: *... can take your..., ... wake-up...,* unspecified verbs: *...take, wake up ...*

(204)

(204)

Take you a while, Nick, to put yourself back together again... And that reorientation to your hands, feeling them again.

Sentence fragment, causal modeling conjunction: *...and...,* referential index: *...a while..., ...that orientation...,* unspecified verb: *...take..., ...put ..., ..back..., ...feeling ...,* presupposition: *... yourself back together again..., ...feeling them again...*

(205)

(205)

And getting your legs, your arms, back to-

Sentence fragment, causal modeling conjunction:

gether, your head back on...Getting acquainted with your body.

...and..., unspecified verbs: *...getting...,* ... *back on...,* *...getting acquainted...*

(206)

(206)

I think it's too comfortable in here.
N: I'm still in a trance.
M: You don't want to come out.
N: Um huh.

Unspecified verb: ... *think...,* deletion: *...too comfortable to whom?* referential index: *...in here...,* deletion: *...too comfortable for whom?*

(207)

(207)

(207-211)

E: No, you don't *want* to *come* out of a trance.

Embedded commands: *...want to come out...,* presupposition: *...you want to...,* nominalization: *...trance...,* unspecified verb: *...want ..., ...come...*

metaphor.

(208)

(208)

You don't *want* a charming movie to *end*, you don't *want* a flower to wilt, but you do *like* reality.

Embedded commands: *...want a charming end ..., ...want...,* *...like reality...,* unspecified verbs: *...want..., ... want..., ...end..., ...like ...,* missing referential index: *...a charming movie..., ...a flower...,* nominalization: *...reality...,* deletions: ... *charming to whom?...*

(209)

(209)

And all I can do is *wonder* how charming you will be at 40, 50, and 60...I can *wonder* at all the new things you will *find* at 40, 50, 60; and I'm looking to find out how nice

Embedded question: ... *wonder...,* unspecified verbs: *...wonder..., ... wonder..., ...find..., ... looking..., ...find...,* missing referential index: *...all the new things..., ...nice things...,* embed-

things are at 80.

ded command: ...*find*...

(210)

(210)

One of my sons told me, "I will be eternally grateful to my grandparents. They taught me that, of course, they had good old times in the past, but the really good times are yet ahead of them."

Missing referential index: ...*one of my sons* ..., ...*good old times*..., ...*in the past*..., ...*really good*..., ...*they*..., ... *they* ..., *them*..., Quotes ..., unspecified verbs: ...*told*..., ...*grateful*..., ...*taught*..., ...*ahead*..., nominalizations: ...*times*..., ...*past* ..., *time*...

(211)

(211)

The first time I learned to ride a horse, I didn't know that one day I'd ride a jet plane; I didn't even know there could be a plane.

Missing referential index: ...*the first time*..., ...*a house*..., ...*one day* ..., ...*a jet plane*..., ...*a plane*..., unspecified verbs: ...*learned*..., ... *know*..., ...*know*.........
presuppositions: ...*first time*...*even*...

(212)

(212)

(212-213)

Now I'm letting you *awaken slowly*, because it's necessary —all people—to *awaken slowly*, and to *let the trance learnings* and thinkings *set*.

Embedded commands: *awaken slowly*..., ... *awaken slowly*..., ...*let the trance*..., ...*learnings* ..., ...*set*..., deletions: ... necessary how for whom? ...*slowly* for whom? ..., referential index: ...*its*..., ...*all people*..., ...*the trance learnings*..., ...*thinkings* ..., unspecified verbs: ... *awaken*..., ...*awaken*..., ...*set*...

re-orientation to present 4-tuple; metaphor.

(213)

(213)

Just like plaster of paris takes a little

Causal modeling, implied causative: ...*just*...,

while to *set*. And after your learnings *get set*, then they will *accompany* you all the rest of your life.

...after..., ...then..., embedded commands: *...set..., ...get set..., ...accompany...,* unspecified verbs: *...takes..., ...set..., ...set..., accompany...,* nominalizations: *...learnings...,* referential index: *...a little while..., ...all the rest..., ...your learnings...,* presuppositions: *all the rest of your life...,* selectional restriction.

(214)

Now for the rest of the day, be unconcerned if you don't seem to be totally in touch with things. You will be adequately in touch for your own welfare and protection.

(214)

Unspecified verbs: *...unconcerned..., ...seem..., ...touch..., ...touch...,* missing referential index: *...things...,* presuppositions: *...for the rest of the day...,* deletion: *...adequately for whom? ...nominalizations:... welfare..., ...protection ...*

(214-223)

meta-instructions to utilize the trance learnings 4-tuples; post-hypnotic suggestions.

(215)

But your unconscious is going to *use up* a lot of your energy sorting over all its past learnings, understandings, and thinking.

(215)

Causal modeling, implied causative: *...but...,* embedded command: *...use up...,* nominalizations: *...unconscious..., ...energy..., learnings..., ...understandings..., ...thinking...,* missing referential index: *...a lot of ..., ...its past learnings ..., ...thinking...,* unspecified verbs: *...use up..., sorting...*

(216)

And it'll *shape it* into something for you to have.

(216)

Causal modeling conjunction: *...and...,* embedded command: ...

shape it..., missing referential index: *...it..., ... it..., ...something...*, unspecified verbs: *...shape ..., ...have...*

(217)

(217)

That takes a little time.

Deletions: *...takes a little time for what/whom? ...*, missing referential index: *...that..., ...a little time...*, nominalization: *...time...*, unspecified verb: *...takes...*, deletion: *...time for what/ whom?...*

(218)

(218)

And by tomorrow morning, you'll be completely awake.

Causal modeling, implied causative: *...and...by ...*, presupposition: *...by tomorrow morning...*, deletion: *...completely for whom?...*, unspecified verb: *...awake...*

(219)

(219)

I want you both have a nice night's sleep, tonight—and if you *wish a pleasant* dream that you may or may not remember.

Unspecified verb: *... want..., ...have..., ... wish..., ...remember...*, embedded command: *... wish a pleasant...*, deletions: *...nice for whom? ..., ...pleasant for whom?...*, causal modeling, implied causative: *...and if...*, missing referential index: *...a pleasant dream...*, nominalization: *...dream...*

(220)

(220)

And I think your unconscious can *give* your conscious mind

Causal modeling conjunction: *...and...*, embedded command: *...*

one special delight—that something you eat for dinner tonight tastes unusually good.

give..., unspecified verbs: ...think..., ...give ..., nominalizations: ... unconscious..., ...conscious mind..., ...delight ..., missing referential index: ...one special delight..., something...unusually good..., deletion: ...good for whom?

(221)

(221)

It'll be your unconscious mind that makes it *taste* unusually good.

Nominalizations: *...unconscious mind..., unspecified verb: ...makes ..., embedded command: ...tastes unusually good..., missing referential index: ...it..., deletion: ...unusually good for whom?*

(222)

(222)

And of course your unconscious may *decide* not the inner; it may *decide* on the feel of the sheets; it may be on something you see.; and your unconscious will make you *feel* unusually pleased.

Causal modeling conjunction: *...and..., embedded commands: ... decide..., ...decide on..., ...feel unusually pleased ..., unspecified verbs: ... decide..., ...decide..., ... see..., ...make..., ...feel ..., ...pleased...*
nominalizations: *...unconscious..., ...unconscious..., missing referential index: ...the dinner..., ...the sheets..., ...something..., deletion: ...unusually compared to what? whom?*

(223)

And now say goodbye to your unconscious, and let's talk and respond to each other at the conscious level. Hi. Hi.

(223)

Causal modeling conjunction: *...and...*, nominalization: *...unconscious...*, *...conscious level...*, unspecified verbs: *...respond...*, presupposition: *...say goodbye to your unconscious...*, *...respond...*, *...at the conscious level ...*, deletion: *...talk about?...*

The following is a discussion of the third level of patterning used by Erickson and describes the systematic way in which Erickson works to access and anchor the client's past 4-tuples, making available the resources needed. This discussion in no way exhausts what is present in Erickson's work, but is to be used to further aid the hypnotist/communicator in both understanding Erickson's work and organizing his or her own experience in hypnosis.

As was earlier stated, one of the single most important patterns for the agent of change (psychotherapeutic practitioner of hypnosis) is the understanding that each of us as human beings has past learnings and understandings that when organized in a directed fashion, provides the resources that a client needs to make the changes he desires.

It is Erickson's use and sequencing of these past 4-tuples that allows him to effect change in such a profound way. As the client makes meaning out of the hypnotist's communication, the client will, in the present, experience the learnings which provide those resources out of the sum total of the client's past 4-tuples. These experiences, (4-tuples) present and past, are then re-arranged in an effective way for the present and future. The understanding of the 4-tuple of primary experience, the transderivation search phenomena, anchoring and effective pacing (meeting the client at his model of the world) will increase the hypnotist's choices greatly in the context of altered states of communication. As Erickson himself states:

...in the therapeutic use of hypnosis, one primarily meets the patient's needs on the terms he himself proposes; and then one fixates the patient's attention, through adequate respect for and utilization of his method of presenting his problem, to his own inner processes of mental functioning. This is accomplished by casual but obviously earnest and sincere remarks, seemingly explanatory but intended solely to stimulate a wealth of the patient's own patterns of psychological functioning so that he meets his problems by use of his learnings already acquired or that he will develop as he continues his progress.

Milton H. Erickson, *Techniques for Resistant Patients*, Haley (ed.), p. 499.

PART III

The preceding transcripts offer a unique opportunity for understanding not only the elegance of Milton Erickson's use of altered states, but they also constitute a complete tracking model for trance induction and change.

At first the transcripts appear to be very different, Erickson's work with Monde is more specific. As in her case he has more verbal and analogical feedback to utilize and assist her in deep trance. Nick offers less in the way of verbal and analogic feedback, and correspondingly, Erickson's work is less specific. With Nick, Erickson utilizes more extensively the general verbal patterns of nominalization, unspecified verbs, missing referential index and deletion in his work.

- accessing (L operator) and anchoring of 4-tuples
- polarity pacing (temperature)
- visual kinesthetic disassociation
- metaphor/meta-instructions
- construction of new 4-tuple - creation of a reference experience
- testing effectiveness of work

In both cases E begins by accessing (L-operator) a past trance 4-tuple,

Monde	Nick
1-3	1-2

as both Nick and Monde begin to access (L-operator) and represent (R-operator) those past 4-tuples, responding to Erickson's communication, they begin to re-experience (both R-operator and ~R) portions of the past trance 4-tuyples (through transderivational search L-operator) phenomena. In other words, portions of the past trance 4-tuples are accessed (L-operator) and re-experienced (R-operator).

Erickson then instructs both clients to attend (R-operator) to the kinesthetic variable of the trance 4-tuple.

Monde	Nick
15-17	9-18
26	49-50
	63

The second meta-pattern is polarity pacing. When pacing a client's ongoing experience, the hypnotist is often presented with inconsistent messages from the client (i.e. the C-operator is no) regarding the trance experience.

It is possible that Erickson was sensitive to mixed messages about the hypnotic experience on Nick's part. One way of effectively pacing in this situation is to pace both parts being presented. In this case the temperature polarity pace can effectively pace the part that desires the trance experience as well as the part that presents a message of resistance. The temperature polarity pace works through metaphor much the way that tag-questions ("you are comfortable, are you not?") pace more directly both messages being presented by the client.

Here we wish to remind the reader that Erickson's work is both subtle and complex. That is just to say that E is utilizing "cool comfort in a hot room" as a very sophisticated polarity pace overlooks other possible understandings. This attention to the kinesthetic variable, namely the 4-tuple = 'comfort' sets a precedent for the client, that he/she may extract the overall formal pattern of, "even though it's hot you can still be comfortable" = "when you are uncomfortable, you can have a choice of being comfortable." This particular pace of comfort-cool, uncomfortable-hot, is parallel in these transcripts with the problems which both clients present; that is, it has a direct application to the problem. Perhaps most importantly it utilizes a piece of the client's ongoing experiences as a continuous pace.

The third pattern to be extracted is that of disassociation and utilization of the disassociated states. This involves the hypnotist's ability to recognize that the variable of experience that the client normally uses for (client's R-Operator) conscious representation to find a point of overlap with the other variables of the 4-tuples which are represented outside of conscious ($\land$R). For example, Erickson instructs Monde to visualize (L-operator) her husband's experience with arm levitation, and then instructs her to generalize what those feelings would be like in her experience (representational system overlap); thereby eliciting arm levitation.

(27-28) In Monde's case Erickson uses the visual variable as lead to re-experiencing other portions of a 4-tuple. In each instance of re-vivication of a pleasant experience, Erickson has Monde, first visualize it, and then add the kinesthetic portion of the 4-tuple, the feelings attached to the pleasant 4-tuple. (81-89,

89-92). Erickson then suggests that Monde recall an unpleasant 4-tuple, again using a visual lead, however, he suggests that she maintain the kinesthetic variable of comfort. (97-101).

With Nick, however, Erickson utilizes Nick's R-system which is kinesthetic and leads him to a point of overlap, whereby he adds the visual portion of the 4-tuple. (43-48) When Erickson works with Nick, he is more general in his hypnotic communication; that is, he does not explicitly ask Nick to recall any particular 4-tuple, but suggests that he maintain the kinesthetic variable (comfort), and visualize any experiences he wishes while holding the K variable constant, maintain K (40-46) (49-50) (53-59).

Metaphor and meta-instruction are the fourth area to be considered. In both transcripts Erickson suggests, to the clients, a new understanding, a new way to experience the world. He does this by offering suggestions directly through metaphor, and through meta-instructions, or a way in which the client may utilize the trance learnings and past 4-tuples with more understanding. This precedent is established early with both clients

Monde	Nick
83-8	83-94
93-96	97-109
174-175	115

to ensure that the meta-instructions are accepted by the client and also to prove to the client that they do have a choice. It is important to demonstrate to the clients that they have the resources to create the choice they want — thus the need to establish a reference experience. The following is an example of the creation of a new reference experience.

Erickson consistently has Monde visualize a past pleasant 4-tuple and then add the kinesthetic variable. Then he instructs her to visualize an unpleasant 4-tuple and hold the kinesthetic variable (of the 1st 4-tuple) constant. Erickson then proves to Monde that she can have control by having her recall an unpleasant 4-tuple using a visual lead, adding the appropriate unpleasant 4-tuple, then to replace the unpleasant kinesthetic sensations with pleasant kinesthetic sensations which have previously been anchored to a piece of Monde's behavior (eye blink). This serves as a reference experience which Monde can utilize at another time.

Monde
116-117
123-131

When Erickson works directly with Nick, he uses a piece of Nick's behavior (breathing) as an illustration and reference experience of how Nick can exercise control over his behavior. As Erickson states, this is something that Nick could notice (namely the absence of loud breathing on Nick's part). Thus the establishing of a reference 4-tuple allows the client a 4-tuple from which they may generalize, and it gives the hypnotist a way in which he/she may check the effectiveness of their work with the client. That is to say that by giving the client a reference 4-tuple which utilizes portions of their own behavior, (eye blink, loud breathing) the hypnotist can literally anchor the client control (consciously or unconsciously) over the new choice. In both cases Erickson does just this. Erickson suggests that Monde practice the self-anchor ("blinking her eyes") to banish discomfort.

The self-anchor of eye blinking, on one level ties the process to a portion of the client's (Monde) ongoing experience, on another level the opening and closing of her eyes to exercise a new choice of comfort may be a metaphor for beginning to really look at her problems.

With Nick, however, Erickson points out his ability to control his breathing as a reference structure rather early in the transcript, and suggests that he maintain his comfort while visualizing different 4-tuples. Finally, he asks Nick directly if he will utilize the new learnings and elicits a direct response from Nick. It is important to note here that Erickson offers suggestions for amnesia throughout both transcripts, thus it is important to understand the means by which only important and useful portions of the trance experience are brought into the conscious state; bridging the gap of experience. This can be understood by having the client exercise the new choice both in the altered state and the waking state. It is in this way that Erickson may check the effectiveness of his work, without forcing the new learnings into the consciousness of the client. Erickson does this by suggesting to Monde that she will experience discomfort (immobile hand, warmth) when she awakens from trance, then Erickson, by use of a behavioral presupposition ("which hand has the longer life line?") allows her to exercise the new choice in controlling the discomfort.

In the preceding section we presented three levels of patterns, the linguistic patterns that constitute the basic foundations of Milton Erickson's use of language in hypnosis, the second level patterns which Erickson uses to achieve a desired level of trance and the desired outcome of suggested phenomenon, and third the level of patterning which illustrates the sequencing and manipulation of past experience (4-tuples), and the incorporation and utilization of the client's ongoing experience to build a reference structure to assist the client in attaining a new choice.

Bibliography

I. General

Bach, E. *Syntactic Theory.* New York: Holt, Rinehart and Winston, Inc., 1974.

Bach-y-Rita, P. *Brain Mechanisms in Sensory Substitution.* New York: Academic Press, 1972.

Bandler, R., and Grinder, J. *The Structure of Magic I.* Palo Alto, Calif.: Science and Behavior Books, 1975.

Bandler, R., Grinder, J., and Satir, V. *Changing with Families,* Volume I, Palo Alto: Science and Behavior Books, Inc., 1976.

Bever, T.G. "The Cognitive Basis of Linguistic Structure," in J. Hayes (ed.), *Cognition and the Developments of Language.* New York: John Wiley and Sons, 1970.

Chomsky, N. *Syntactic Structures.* Mouton, The Hague, 1957.

Chomsky, N. *Language and Mind.* New York: Harcourt Brace Jovanovich, Inc., 1968.

Dimond, S., and Beaumont, K. *Hemisphere Function in the Human Brain.* New York: John Wiley & Sons, 1974.

Dimond, S. *The Double Brain.* London: Churchill Livingstone, 1972.

Eccles, J. *Brain and Conscious Experience.* New York: Springer-Verlag, 1966.

Fillmore, C., "The Case for Case," in E. Bach and R. Harms (eds.), *Universals in Linguistic Theory.* New York: Holt, Rinehart and Winston, 1968.

Gardner, H. *The Shattered Mind,* Knopf, 1975.

Gazzainga, M. *The Bisected Brain.* New York: Appleton Century Croft, 1974.

Greene, G. "How to Get People to Do Things With Words," in *Papers From the 8th Regional Meeting of the Chicago Linguistic Society.* Chicago: University of Chicago, 1970.

Grinder, J. *On Deletion Phenomena in English.* Mouton, The Hague, 1974.

Grinder, J. and Bandler, R. *The Structure of Magic II,* Palo Alto: Science and Behavior Books, Inc., 1976.

Grinder, J., Bandler, R. and Cameron, L, *Neuro Linguistic Programming I,* (in preparation).

Grinder, J., and Elgin, S. *A Guide to Transformational Grammar.* New York: Holt, Rinehart and Winston, 1973.

Gruber, J. "Studies in Lexical Relations." Unpublished doctoral dissertation, MIT, 1965.

Haley,[1], J. (ed.) *Advanced Techniques of Hypnosis and Therapy.* New York: Grune and Stratton, 1967.

Haley, J. *Uncommon Therapy.* New York: Grune and Stratton.

Horn, L. "A Presuppositional Analysis of *Only* and *Even*," in *Papers From the 5th Regional Meeting of the Chicago Linguistic Society.* Chicago: University of Chicago, 1969.

Jacobs, R., and Rosenbaum, P. *English Transformational Grammar.* Waltham, Mass.: Ginn/Blaisdell, 1968.

Jeffress, J.A. *Cerebral Mechanisms in Behavior.* New York: Hafner Co., 1967.

Kartunnen, L. "Remarks on Presuppositions," at the Texas Conference on Performances, Conversational Implicature and Presuppositions, March 1973, mimeograph.

Katz, J. *Semantic Theory.* New York: Harper and Row, 1972.

Lakoff, G. *Linguistics and Natural Logic.* Ann Arbor: University Michigan, 1970.

Langacker, R. *Language and Its Structure.* New York: Harcourt Brace Jovanovich, Inc., 1967.

Levy, J. "Psychobiological Implications of Bilateral Asymmetry," article in *Hemisphere Function in the Human Brain.* New York: John Wiley & Sons, 1974.

Lyons, J. *Introduction to Theoretical Linguistics.* Cambridge, England: Cambridge University Press.

McCawley, J. "Lexical Insertion in a Transformational Grammar," in *Papers From the 4th Regional Meeting of the Chi-*

cago Linguistic Society. Chicago: University of Chicago, 1968.

Miller, G.A., "The Magic Number 7 ≠ 2" in the *American Psychologist*, 1956.

Plath, W., and Bever, T. *Specification and Utilization of a Transformational Grammar.* Bedford, Mass.: Air Force Cambridge Research Laboratories, July 1968.

Polya, G. *Patterns of Plausible Inference.* Princeton, N.J.: Princeton Univ. Press, 1954.

Postal, P. "On the Derivaton of Pseudo-Adjectives," paper delivered to the 44th Annual Meeting of the LSA, 1969.

Postal, P. "On the Surface Verb *Remind,*" in *Linguistic Inquiry.* (1;1:37-120) 1970.

Ross, J.R. "On Declarative Sentences," in R. Jacobs and P. Rosenbaum, *Readings in English Transformational Grammar.* Waltham, Mass.: Ginn/Blaisdell, 1970.

Sapir, E. *The Selected Writing of Edward Sapir.* Berkeley: University of California Press, D. Mandelbaum(ed.), 1963.

Searle, J. *Speech Acts.* Cambridge, England: Cambridge University Press, 1969.

Weizenhoffer, A. *General Techniques of Hypnotism.* New York: Grune and Stratton, 1957.

Whorf, B. "Grammatical Categories," in J.E. Carroll (ed.), *Language, Thought and Reality.* New York: John Wiley and Sons, 1956.

II. Modeling/Formal Systems/Epistemology

Ashby, W.R. *An Introduction to Cybernetics.* Chapman and Hall, Ltd., and University Paperbacks, 1956.

Bateson, G. *Steps to an Ecology of Mind.* New York: Ballantine Books, 1972.

Boyd, D. *Introduction to Systems Analysis.* (in press) 1975.

Carnap, R. *The Logical Syntax of Language.* Totowa, New Jersey: Littlefield, Adams and Company, 1959.

Copi, I. *Introduction to Logic.* New York: Macmillan, 1961.

Herzberger, H. "The Logical Consistency of Language," in *Harvard Educational Review*, 35:469-480, 1965.

Hume, D. *Enquiry Concerning Human Understanding.* Oxford, England: Oxford University Press.

Korzybski, A. *Science and Sanity.* Lakeville, Conn.: The International Non-Aristotelian Library Publishing Company, 4th Edition, 1933.

Miller, G. A.; Galanter, E.; and Pribram, K. *Plans and the Structure of Behavior.* New York: Holt, Rinehart and Winston, Inc., 1960.

Newell, A.; and Simon, H. A. *Human Problem Solving.* Englewood Cliffs, New Jersey: Prentice-Hall, 1972.

Pribram, K. *Language of the Brain.* Englewood Cliffs, New Jersey: Prentice-Hall, 1971.

Russell, B. *Introduction to Mathematical Philosophy.* London, England: George Allen and Unwin, Ltd., 2nd Edition, 1921.

Schank, R.; and Colby, K. *Computer Models of Thought and Language.* San Francisco: W.H. Freeman and Company, 1973.

Tarski, A. *Introduction to Logic.* New York: Oxford University Press, 1941.

Vaihinger, H. *The Philosophy of "As If."* London, England: Routledge, Kegan and Paul, Ltd., 1924.

---

1. References labeled "(Milton H. Erickson) 1967" refer to Haley (ed.), 1967.

WARNING TO THE READER

Neuro Linguistic Programming (NLP) represents a significant advance in the development of human choice. It places at the discretion of the skilled and balanced practitioner options for living with quality which were previously assigned variously to fate, chance, genetics, accidents and divine influence. It is important to me to explicate at least partially what I intend by the descriptive phrase, *skilled and balanced.*

The *skill* issue points to the requirement in the mastery of any interesting human skill set for a commitment to practice, the personal discipline on the part of the would-be NLP practitioner to arrange his or her own context for exploring, learning and ultimately mastering of the actual body of patterning called NLP. Success at this task identifies a learner, and the result a technician.

The *balanced* issue refers to two requirements, first, the learner's ability to integrate the skill set (mastered by the technician) into each and every area of their life, personal as well as professional. Secondly, once this integration of the technical skill set has occurred, the individual is faced with the awesome responsibility of exercising these choices with some wisdom. At this point, the caterpillar bursts the confinement of the cocoon, the technician transforms herself/himself into an artist.

All the above is a somewhat circuitous way of cautioning the would-be NLP practitioner. The world at the moment seems rather overflowing with people purporting to offer training in NLP. It is here in selecting a mentor that you, the reader, may begin to exercise one of the most crucial abilities associated with artistry in the practice of NLP—namely, that of assessing the congruency of the purported trainer. If your intuitions caution you, if you detect a discrepancy between the verbal presentation of such a person and their actual behavior and performance, keep moving and looking for an appropriate model.

If you are seriously interested in having access to quality training or business consulting applications which rest firmly on the foundation of NLP which I intended when I co-created the discipline, I invite you to contact me at:

John Grinder
QUANTUM LEAP
PO Box 67359
Scotts Valley, CA 95067-7359
TEL) 408-457-0529
FAX) 408-457-2834

Grinder & Associates
• Books

A Framework For Excellence: A Resource Manual For NLP
Charlotte Bretto Milliner
ISBN 0-929514-03-3 PB

Leaves Before The Wind
Charlotte Bretto Milliner, Judith DeLozier, John Grinder & Sylvia Topel, eds.
ISBN 1-55552-051-0 PB

**Making The Message Clear: How To Master The
Business Communication Tools That Direct Productivity,
Excellence and Power**
James Eicher
ISBN 1-55552-048-0 PB

**Patterns of the Hypnotic Techniques of Milton H. Erickson, M.D.,
Vol. I**
Richard Bandler & John Grinder
ISBN 1-55552-052-9 PB

**Patterns of the Hypnotic Techniques of Milton H. Erickson, M.D.,
Vol. II**
John Grinder, Judith DeLozier & Richard Bandler
ISBN 1-55552-053-7 PB

Practical Magic
Stephen R. Lankton, ACSW
ISBN 0-916990-08-7 PB

Precision: A New Approach To Communication
Michael McMaster & John Grinder
ISBN 1-55552-049-9 PB

Turtles All The Way Down: Prerequisites To Personal Genius
John Grinder & Judith DeLozier
ISBN 1-55552-022-7 HB

Grinder & Associates
• Audio

The Syntax of Behavior Series I
Presented by John Grinder & Robert Dilts
Volume 1: States and Strategies. 8 tapes
Volume 2: Anchoring: The Oldest Mystery in NLP. 8 tapes
Volume 3: Belief Systems: Methods For Change. 8 tapes
Volume 4: A Batesonian Model For Investigation. 8 tapes

The Syntax of Behavior Series II
Presented by John Grinder & Steven Gilligan
Volume 1: Tools For Mind Mastery: Meeting Life Challenges
  With Wisdom. 6 tapes
Volume 2: Generative Personality: Enjoying The Present
  & Building The Future. 7 tapes

Advanced Modeling
Replete with exercises designed to prepare you for effective modeling. The listener is led through a series of experiences which assist to create the state highly valued in the pursuit of accelerated learning. 14 tapes

Modeling The Healing Process
This series features John Grinder leading participants through the latest exercises in NLP modeling technlogy. Methods of creating optimal states for responding to healing interventions are also demonstrated. 7 tapes

Training Trainers
Designed for experienced NLP practitioners, this series covers the topic of state preparation and presuppositions of training, including the use of metaphor and congruity requirements of the presenter. 12 tapes

METAMORphous
AdvANCEd
PRoduct
SERVICES

METAMORphous AdvANCEd PRoduct SERVICES (M.A.P.S.) is the master distributor for Metamorphous Press and other fine publishers.

M.A.P.S. offers books, cassettes, videos, software, and miscellaneous products in the following subjects: Business & Sales, Children, Education, Enneagram, Health (including Alexander Technique and Rolfing), Hypnosis, Personal Development, Psychology (including Neurolinguistic Programming), and Relationships/Sexuality.

If you cannot find our books at your favorite bookstore, you can order directly from M.A.P.S.

TO ORDER OR REQUEST A FREE CATALOG:

MAIL   M.A.P.S.
P.O. Box 10616
Portland, OR 97296-0616

FAX   (503) 223-9117

CALL   Toll free 1-800-233-6277

ALL OTHER BUSINESS:

CALL   (503) 228-4972

Printed in the United States
29893LVS00006B/16-18

9 781555 520533